HOUGHTON MIFFLIN HARCOURT

MATH Expressions
Common Core

Dr. Karen C. Fuson

GRADE 2

This material is based upon work supported by the
National Science Foundation
under Grant Numbers
ESI-9816320, REC-9806020, and RED-935373.

Any opinions, findings, and conclusions, or recommendations expressed in this material
are those of the author and do not necessarily reflect the views of the National Science Foundation.

HOUGHTON MIFFLIN HARCOURT

TEACHER'S RESOURCE BOOK

CONTENTS

CONTENTS continued

Family Letter

Dear Family:

Your child is learning math in a program called *Math Expressions,* which links mathematical ideas to a child's everyday experiences. This helps children understand math better.

In this program, your child will learn math and have fun by

- working with objects and making drawings of math situations.
- listening to and working with other children and sharing ways to solve problems.
- writing and solving problems and connecting math to daily life.
- helping classmates learn.

Your child will have homework almost every day. He or she needs a Homework Helper. The helper may be anyone—a family member, an older brother or sister, a neighbor, or a friend. Set aside a definite time for homework and provide your child with a quiet place to work where there are no distractions. Encourage your child to talk about what is happening in math class. If your child is having problems with math, please talk to me to see how you might help.

Please cut, fill in, and return the bottom part of this letter.

Thank you. You are very important to your child's learning.

Sincerely,
Your child's teacher

COMMON CORE
Unit 1 includes the Common Core Standards for Mathematical Content for Operations and Algebraic Thinking 2.OA.1, 2.OA.2, 2.OA.3, Numbers and Operations in Base Ten 2.NBT.5, 2.NBT.6, 2.NBT.9, and all Mathematical Practices.

My child _____ will have
(child's name)

_____ as a Homework Helper.
(name of homework helper)

This person is my child's _____.
(relationship to child)

_____
signature of parent or guardian

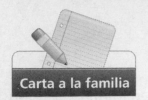

Carta a la familia

Estimada familia:

Su niño está aprendiendo matemáticas con un programa llamado *Math Expressions*, que relaciona conceptos matemáticos abstractos con la experiencia diaria de los niños. Esto ayuda a los niños a entender mejor las matemáticas.

Con este programa, su niño va a aprender matemáticas y se divertirá mientras:

- trabaja con objetos y hace dibujos de situaciones matemáticas.
- escucha y trabaja con otros estudiantes y comparte con ellos estrategias para resolver problemas.
- escribe y resuelve problemas, y relaciona las matemáticas con la vida diaria.
- ayuda a sus compañeros de clase a aprender.

Su niño tendrá tarea casi todos los días y necesitará que alguna persona lo ayude. Esa persona puede ser, usted, un hermano mayor, un vecino o un amigo. Establezca una hora para la tarea y ofrezca a su niño un lugar donde trabajar sin distracciones. Anímelo a comentar lo que está aprendiendo en la clase de matemáticas. Si él tiene problemas con las matemáticas, hable por favor con el maestro para ver cómo puede usted ayudar.

Por favor recorte, complete y devuelva el formulario al maestro.

Muchas gracias. Usted es imprescindible en el aprendizaje de su niño.

Atentamente,
El maestro de su niño

COMMON CORE

La Unidad 1 incluye los Common Core Standards for Mathematical Content for Operations and Algebraic Thinking 2.OA.1, 2.OA.2, 2.OA.3, Numbers and Operations in Base Ten 2.NBT.5, 2.NBT.6, 2.NBT.9, and all Mathematical Practices.

La persona que ayudará a mi niño _____ es
(nombre del niño)

_____. Esta persona es
(nombre de la persona)

_____ de mi niño.
(relación con el niño)

_____
Su firma

Family Letter

Dear Family:

Your child is exploring addition and subtraction equations with Math Mountain Cards. The cards have a large number at the top and two smaller numbers at the bottom. From the cards, children can see that two smaller numbers can be added together to make a larger number. They can also see that a large number can be broken apart into two smaller numbers.

Children will write addition and subtraction equations that they can make from the cards, as shown in the example. The two partners, 9 and 6, can be added to make the total, 15. They can be switched (6 and 9) and still make 15.

$9 + 6 = 15$ $15 = 9 + 6$

$6 + 9 = 15$ $15 = 6 + 9$

$15 - 9 = 6$ $6 = 15 - 9$

$15 - 6 = 9$ $9 = 15 - 6$

15

— —

9   +   6

Students see and write all eight equations. It is important for understanding algebra that they sometimes see equations with only one number on the left.

Please call if you need practice materials. Thank you for helping your child learn about the relationship between addition and subtraction.

Sincerely,
Your child's teacher

COMMON CORE

Unit 1 includes the Common Core Standards for Mathematical Content for Operations and Algebraic Thinking 2.OA.1, 2.OA.2, 2.OA.3, Numbers and Operations in Base Ten 2.NBT.5, 2.NBT.6, 2.NBT.9, and all Mathematical Practices.

Estimada familia:

Su niño está aprendiendo ecuaciones de suma y resta usando las tarjetas *Math Mountain*. Las tarjetas tienen un número grande en la parte superior y dos números más pequeños en la parte inferior. En las tarjetas los niños pueden ver que se pueden sumar dos números más pequeños para obtener un número más grande. También pueden ver que un número grande se puede separar en dos números más pequeños.

Los niños escribirán ecuaciones de suma y resta que puedan hacer a partir de las tarjetas, según se muestra en el ejemplo. Se pueden sumar las dos partes, 9 y 6, para obtener el total, 15. También se pueden intercambiar (6 y 9) y todavía obtener 15.

$9 + 6 = 15$

$6 + 9 = 15$

$15 - 9 = 6$

$15 - 6 = 9$

$$15$$
$$- \quad -$$
$$9 \quad + \quad 6$$

$15 = 9 + 6$

$15 = 6 + 9$

$6 = 15 - 9$

$9 = 15 - 6$

Los estudiantes ven y escriben las ocho ecuaciones. Para comprender álgebra es importante que vean ecuaciones con un solo número a la izquierda.

Por favor comuníquese conmigo si necesita materiales para practicar. Gracias por ayudar a su niño a aprender la relación entre suma y resta.

Atentamente,
El maestro de su niño

COMMON CORE

La Unidad 1 incluye los Common Core Standards for Mathematical Content for Operations and Algebraic Thinking 2.OA.1, 2.OA.2, 2.OA.3, Numbers and Operations in Base Ten 2.NBT.5, 2.NBT.6, 2.NBT.9, and all Mathematical Practices.

Dear Family:

Your child is learning to solve word problems called *Add To* and *Take From* problems. These problems begin with a quantity that is then modified by change—something is added or subtracted—which results in a new quantity.

Proof drawings show what your child was thinking when solving the problem. It is important that children label their drawings to link them to the problem situation.

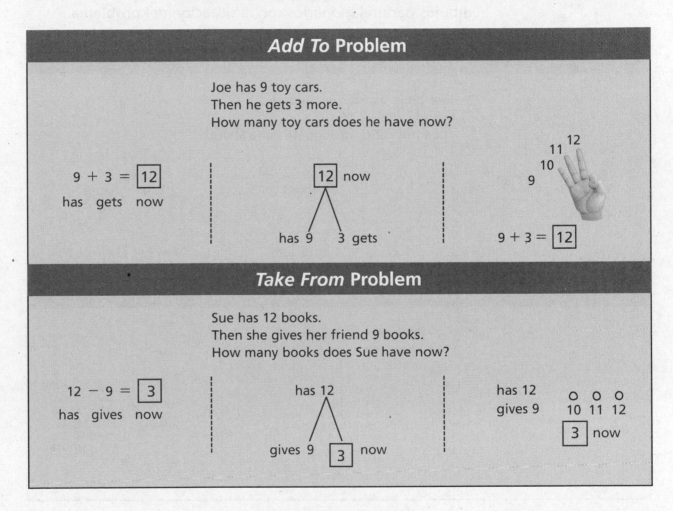

Add To Problem

Joe has 9 toy cars.
Then he gets 3 more.
How many toy cars does he have now?

$9 + 3 = \boxed{12}$

has gets now

$\boxed{12}$ now

has 9   3 gets

$9 + 3 = \boxed{12}$

Take From Problem

Sue has 12 books.
Then she gives her friend 9 books.
How many books does Sue have now?

$12 - 9 = \boxed{3}$

has gives now

has 12

gives 9 $\boxed{3}$ now

has 12
gives 9   ○ ○ ○
           10 11 12
           $\boxed{3}$ now

Please call if you have any questions or concerns.

Sincerely,
Your child's teacher

COMMON CORE Unit 1 includes the Common Core Standards for Mathematical Content for Operations and Algebraic Thinking 2.OA.1, 2.OA.2, 2.OA.3, Numbers and Operations in Base Ten 2.NBT.5, 2.NBT.6, 2.NBT.9, and all Mathematical Practices.

Carta a la familia

Estimada familia:

Su niño está aprendiendo a resolver problemas conocidos como problemas de *cambio al sumar* o de *cambio al restar*. Estos empiezan con una cantidad que luego es modificada por un cambio (algo que se suma o se resta), lo que resulta en una nueva cantidad.

Los dibujos muestran lo que su niño estaba pensando mientras resolvía el problema. Es importante que los niños rotulen sus dibujos para relacionarlos con la situación del problema.

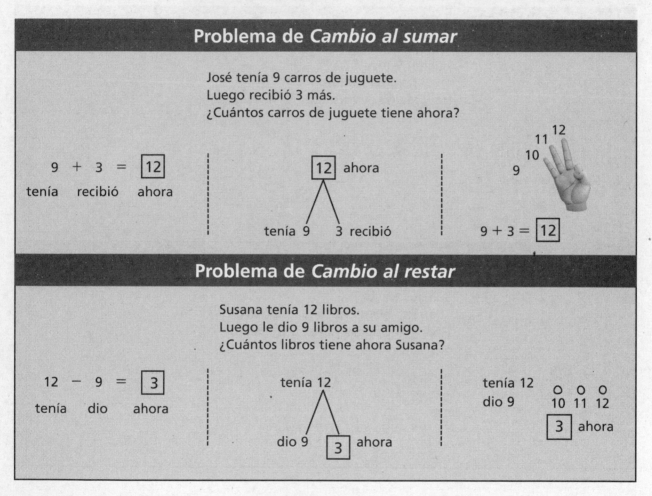

Problema de *Cambio al sumar*

José tenía 9 carros de juguete.
Luego recibió 3 más.
¿Cuántos carros de juguete tiene ahora?

$9 + 3 = \boxed{12}$
tenía recibió ahora

$\boxed{12}$ ahora
tenía 9   3 recibió

11 12
10
9
$9 + 3 = \boxed{12}$

Problema de *Cambio al restar*

Susana tenía 12 libros.
Luego le dio 9 libros a su amigo.
¿Cuántos libros tiene ahora Susana?

$12 - 9 = \boxed{3}$
tenía dio ahora

tenía 12
dio 9 $\boxed{3}$ ahora

tenía 12
dio 9   o o o
      10 11 12
      $\boxed{3}$ ahora

Si tiene alguna pregunta o algún comentario, por favor comuníquese conmigo.

Atentamente,
El maestro de su niño

COMMON CORE

La Unidad 1 incluye los Common Core Standards for Mathematical Content for Operations and Algebraic Thinking 2.OA.1, 2.OA.2, 2.OA.3, Numbers and Operations in Base Ten 2.NBT.5, 2.NBT.6, 2.NBT.9, and all Mathematical Practices.

Dear Family:

Your child is learning about place value and will use this knowledge to add 2- and 3-digit numbers.

As we begin this unit, your child will represent numbers using drawings like this one:

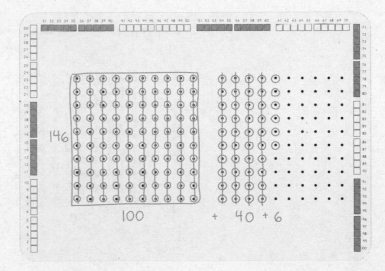

Then, children will begin to represent numbers using Quick Hundreds and Quick Tens.

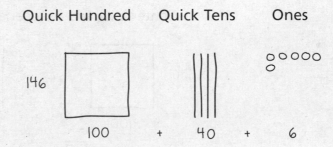

Quick Hundred	Quick Tens	Ones
146		
100	+ 40	+ 6

Name a 2- or 3-digit number and ask your child to make a drawing to represent that number.

Later in this unit, children will work on adding 2-digit numbers using the drawings to help them.

Thank you. Please call or write if you have any questions.

Sincerely,
Your child's teacher

Unit 2 includes the Common Core Standards for Mathematical Content for Operations and Algebraic Thinking, 2.OA.1, 2.OA.2; Number and Operations in Base Ten, 2.NBT.1, 2.NBT.1a, 2.NBT.1b, 2.NBT.2, 2.NBT.3, 2.NBT.4, 2.NBT.5, 2.NBT.6, 2.NBT.7, 2.NBT.8, 2.NBT.9; Measurement and Data, MD.8; and all Mathematical Practices.

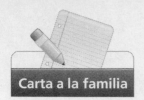

Carta a la familia

Estimada familia:

Su niño está aprendiendo acerca del valor posicional y usará esos conocimientos para sumar números de 2 y 3 dígitos.

Cuando comencemos con esta unidad, su niño representará números usando dibujos como este:

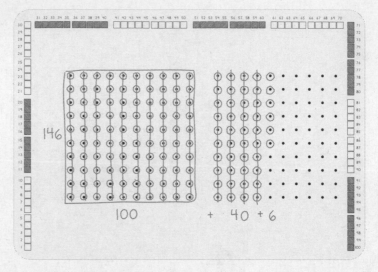

Luego, los niños comenzarán a representar números usando "Centenas rápidas" y "Decenas rápidas".

Centena rápida   Decenas rápidas   Unidades

146   100   +   40   +   6

Diga un número de 2 ó 3 dígitos y pida a su niño que haga un dibujo para representar ese número.

Más adelante, los niños trabajarán sumando números de 2 dígitos y usarán los dibujos como ayuda.

Gracias. Si tiene alguna pregunta, por favor comuníquese conmigo.

Atentamente,
El maestro de su niño

COMMON CORE

La Unidad 2 incluye los Common Core Standards for Mathematical Content for Operations and Algebraic Thinking, 2.OA.1, 2.OA.2; Number and Operations in Base Ten, 2.NBT.1, 2.NBT.1a, 2.NBT.1b, 2.NBT.2, 2.NBT.3, 2.NBT.4, 2.NBT.5, 2.NBT.6, 2.NBT.7, 2.NBT.8, 2.NBT.9; Measurement and Data, MD.8; and all Mathematical Practices.

Dear Family:

Your child is now learning how to add 2-digit numbers. The "big mystery" in adding is making a new ten or a new hundred. Children can write this new group in several ways.

Show All Totals	New Groups Below
$$\begin{array}{r} 45 \\ +\ 28 \\ \hline \end{array}$$ Add tens. → 60 Add ones. → 13 $\overline{73}$ Find total tens. Find total ones.	$$\begin{array}{r} 45 \\ +\ 28 \\ \hline 73 \end{array}$$ New ten Find total ones. (13) Write 3 and put the new ten in the tens column ready to add. Add the tens. (4 + 2 = 6, 6 + 1 = 7)

New ten (Show All Totals)

Children usually find it easier to write the new ten below because then they add the new ten last. They add 4 + 2 = 6 and then 6 + 1 = 7.

Traditionally, most children have learned to write the new ten above. With this method, you add 1 + 4 = 5 and then 5 + 2 = 7. This is more difficult for many children, but some children may still choose this method, particularly if they have been taught to do so previously.

Thank you for helping your child learn mathematics.

New Groups Above

$$\begin{array}{r} 1 \\ 45 \\ +\ 28 \\ \hline 73 \end{array}$$

Sincerely,
Your child's teacher

Unit 2 includes the Common Core Standards for Mathematical Content for Operations and Algebraic Thinking, 2.OA.1, 2.OA.2; Number and Operations in Base Ten, 2.NBT.1, 2.NBT.1a, 2.NBT.1b, 2.NBT.2, 2.NBT.3, 2.NBT.4, 2.NBT.5, 2.NBT.6, 2.NBT.7, 2.NBT.8, 2.NBT.9; Measurement and Data, MD.8; and all Mathematical Practices.

COMMON CORE

Estimada familia:

Su niño está aprendiendo a sumar números de 2 dígitos. El "gran misterio" en la suma de números de 2 dígitos consiste en formar una nueva decena o una nueva centena. Los niños pueden anotar este nuevo grupo de varias maneras.

Mostrar todos los totales	Grupos nuevos abajo
45 + 28 Sumar decenas. → 60 Sumar unidades. → 13 73 Hallar el total de decenas. Hallar el total de unidades. Nueva decena	45 + 28 73 Nueva decena Hallar el total de unidades. (13) Escribir 3 y poner la nueva decena en la columna de las decenas, lista para sumar. Sumar las decenas. (4 + 2 = 6, 6 + 1 = 7)

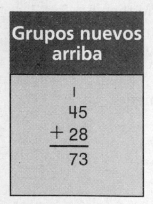

Grupos nuevos arriba
1 45 + 28 73

Por lo general a los niños les resulta más fácil escribir la nueva decena abajo, porque entonces suman la nueva decena al final. Suman 4 + 2 = 6 y luego 6 + 1 = 7.

Tradicionalmente, la mayoría de los estudiantes han aprendido a escribir la nueva decena arriba. Con ese método, se suma 1 + 4 = 5 y luego 5 + 2 = 7. Para muchos niños ese método resulta más difícil pero algunos siguen escogiéndolo, en especial si ya lo han aprendido.

Gracias por ayudar a su niño a aprender matemáticas.

Atentamente,
El maestro de su niño

COMMON CORE

La Unidad 2 incluye los Common Core Standards for Mathematical Content for Operations and Algebraic Thinking, 2.OA.1, 2.OA.2; Number and Operations in Base Ten, 2.NBT.1, 2.NBT.1a, 2.NBT.1b, 2.NBT.2, 2.NBT.3, 2.NBT.4, 2.NBT.5, 2.NBT.6, 2.NBT.7, 2.NBT.8, 2.NBT.9; Measurement and Data, MD.8; and all Mathematical Practices.

Dear Family:

Your child is working on a geometry and measurement unit. In this unit, children will use centimeter rulers to measure line segments and draw shapes.

You can help your child link geometry concepts learned in school with the real world. Encourage your child to find examples of different shapes (triangles, quadrilaterals including rectangles and squares, pentagons, and hexagons) in your home or neighborhood. This will help your child enjoy and understand geometry.

In Lesson 1 of this unit, your child will be asked to find the partner lengths of a line segment. An example is shown below.

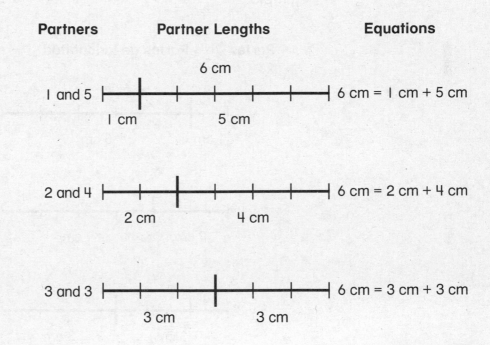

Partners	Partner Lengths	Equations
1 and 5	6 cm / 1 cm / 5 cm	6 cm = 1 cm + 5 cm
2 and 4	2 cm / 4 cm	6 cm = 2 cm + 4 cm
3 and 3	3 cm / 3 cm	6 cm = 3 cm + 3 cm

If you have any questions or comments, please call or write to me. Thank you.

Sincerely,
Your child's teacher

Unit 3 includes the Common Core Standards for Mathematical Content for Operations and Algebraic Thinking 2.OA.2, Number and Operations in Base Ten 2.NBT.4, 2.NBT.5, 2.NBT.6, Geometry 2.G.1, Measurement and Data 2.MD.1, 2.MD.2, 2.MD.3, 2.MD.4, 2.MD.9, and all Mathematical Practices.

Estimada familia:

Su niño está trabajando en una unidad que trata sobre geometría y medidas. En esta unidad los niños usarán reglas en centímetros para medir segmentos y trazar figuras.

Usted puede ayudar a su niño a relacionar los conceptos de geometría que aprenda en la escuela con el mundo real. Anímelo a buscar ejemplos de diferentes figuras (triángulos, cuadriláteros incluyendo rectángulos y cuadrados, pentágonos y hexágonos), en su casa o en el vecindario. Esto ayudará a su niño a disfrutar y a comprender la geometría.

En la Lección 1 de esta unidad se le pedirá a su niño que halle las partes de la longitud de un segmento. Abajo se muestra un ejemplo.

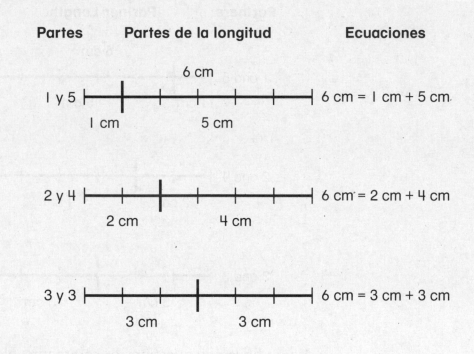

Partes	Partes de la longitud	Ecuaciones
1 y 5	6 cm / 1 cm / 5 cm	6 cm = 1 cm + 5 cm
2 y 4	2 cm / 4 cm	6 cm = 2 cm + 4 cm
3 y 3	3 cm / 3 cm	6 cm = 3 cm + 3 cm

Si tiene alguna pregunta o algún comentario, por favor comuníquese conmigo. Gracias.

Atentamente,
El maestro de su niño

COMMON CORE

La Unidad 3 incluye los Common Core Standards for Mathematical Content for Operations and Algebraic Thinking 2.OA.2, Number and Operations in Base Ten 2.NBT.4, 2.NBT.5, 2.NBT.6, Geometry 2.G.1, Measurement and Data 2.MD.1, 2.MD.2, 2.MD.3, 2.MD.4, 2.MD.9, and all Mathematical Practices.

Dear Family:

In this unit, your child will be collecting measurement data and using that data to make line plots. A *line plot* is a display that uses a number line and dots (or other marks) to represent data. For this reason, line plots are sometimes called *dot plots*.

Your child will be asked to bring one or two pencils to school. The length of each pencil should be more than 1 inch and less than 8 inches. Children will work in small groups. They will measure each pencil brought in by the members of their group and then make a line plot similar to the one shown below.

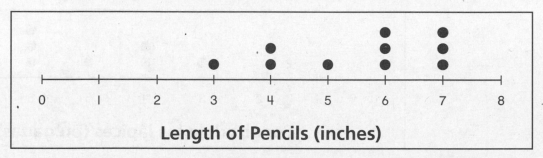

Length of Pencils (inches)

In this unit, your child will also be given several experiences that will help build understanding that the smaller the unit used to measure a given length or distance, the more of those units will be needed.

So, for example, since centimeters are shorter than inches, when the paintbrush below is measured in both centimeters and inches, the number of centimeters is more than the number of inches.

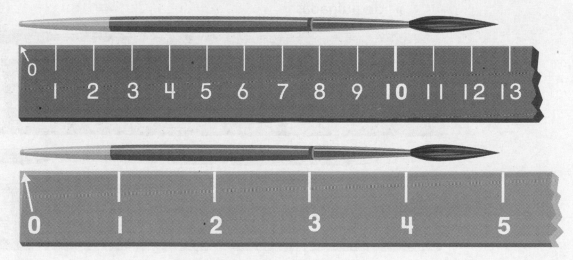

Sincerely,
Your child's teacher

Unit 3 includes the Common Core Standards for Mathematical Content for Operations and Algebraic Thinking 2.OA.2, Numbers and Operations in Base Ten 2.NBT.4, 2.NBT.5, 2.NBT.6, Geometry 2.G.1, Measurement and Data 2.MD.1, 2.MD.2, 2.MD.3, 2.MD.4, 2.MD.9, and all Mathematical Practices.

Estimada familia:

En esta unidad, su niño reunirá datos sobre medidas y usará esos datos para hacer diagramas de puntos. Un *diagrama de puntos* es un diagrama que usa una recta numérica y puntos u otras marcas para representar datos.

Se le pedirá a su niño que traiga uno o dos lápices a la escuela. Cada lápiz debe medir más de 1 pulgada de longitud pero menos de 8. Los niños trabajarán en grupos pequeños. Medirán los lápices de cada miembro de su grupo y luego, harán un diagrama de puntos como el que se muestra debajo.

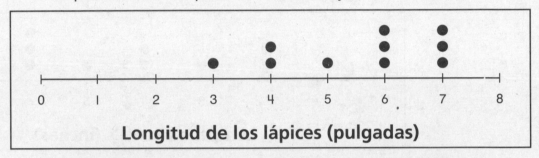

Longitud de los lápices (pulgadas)

También en esta unidad, a su niño se le brindarán diversas experiencias que lo ayudarán a comprender que entre más pequeña sea la unidad que se use para medir una determinada longitud o distancia, más de esas unidades se necesitarán.

Entonces, por ejemplo, como los centímetros son más cortos que las pulgadas, cuando el pincel de abajo se mide en centímetros y en pulgadas, el número de centímetros es mayor que el número de pulgadas.

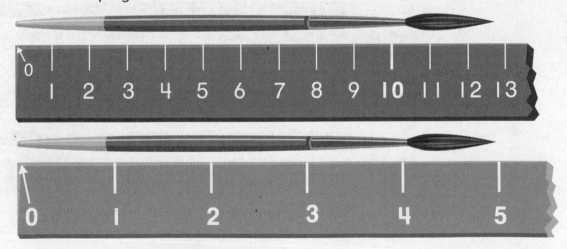

Atentamente,
El maestro de su niño

COMMON CORE

La Unidad 3 incluye los Common Core Standards for Mathematical Content for Operations and Algebraic Thinking 2.OA.2, Numbers and Operations in Base Ten 2.NBT.4, 2.NBT.5, 2.NBT.6, Geometry 2.G.1, Measurement and Data 2.MD.1, 2.MD.2, 2.MD.3, 2.MD.4, 2.MD.9, and all Mathematical Practices.

Family Letter

Dear Family:

In this unit, your child will find the value of various coin combinations. Children will also combine different coins to equal one dollar.

$$25¢ + 25¢ + 10¢ + 10¢ + 10¢ + 10¢ + 10¢ = 100¢$$

Then your child will count both dollars and coins.

Say: $1.00 $1.25 $1.35 $1.40

You can help at home by providing opportunities for your child to practice counting money. Begin with amounts less than $1.00.

Please call if you have any questions or concerns. Thank you for helping your child to learn mathematics.

Sincerely,
Your child's teacher

COMMON CORE Unit 4 includes the Common Core Standards for Mathematical Content for Operations and Algebraic Thinking, 2.OA.1, 2.OA.2; Number and Operations in Base Ten, 2.NBT.4, 2.NBT.5, 2.NBT.6, 2.NBT.7, 2.NBT.8, 2.NBT.9; Measurement and Data, 2.MD.8; and all Mathematical Practices.

Estimada familia:

En esta unidad su niño va a hallar el valor de diversas combinaciones de monedas. Los niños también combinarán diferentes monedas para igualar el valor de un dólar.

25¢ + 25¢ + 10¢ + 10¢ + 10¢ + 10¢ + 10¢ =   100¢

Luego, su niño contará billetes de dólares y monedas.

Se dice: $1.00 $1.25 $1.35 $1.40

Usted puede ayudar a su niño proporcionándole en casa oportunidades de practicar contando dinero. Empiece con cantidades menores que $1.00.

Si tiene alguna duda o algún comentario, por favor comuníquese conmigo. Gracias por ayudar a su niño a aprender matemáticas.

Atentamente,
El maestro de su niño

COMMON CORE

La Unidad 4 incluye los Common Core Standards for Mathematical Content for Operations and Algebraic Thinking, 2.OA.1, 2.OA.2; Number and Operations in Base Ten, 2.NBT.4, 2.NBT.5, 2.NBT.6, 2.NBT.7, 2.NBT.8, 2.NBT.9; Measurement and Data, 2.MD.8; and all Mathematical Practices.

Family Letter

Dear Family:

In this program, children learn these two methods for 2-digit subtraction. However, children may use any method that they understand, can explain, and can do fairly quickly.

Expanded Method	**Ungroup First Method**
Step 1 "Expand" each number to show that it is made up of tens and ones. $$64 = 60 + 4$$ $$-28 = 20 + 8$$ **Step 2** Check to see if there are enough ones to subtract from. If not, ungroup a ten into 10 ones and add it to the existing ones. $$\overset{50}{64} = \overset{}{\cancel{60}} + \overset{14}{\cancel{4}}$$ $$-28 = 20 + 8$$ **Step 3** Subtract to find the answer. Children may subtract from left to right or from right to left. $$\overset{50}{64} = \cancel{60} + \overset{14}{\cancel{4}}$$ $$-28 = 20 + 8$$ $$30 + 6 = 36$$	**Step 1** Check to see if there are enough ones to subtract from. If not, ungroup by opening up one of the 6 tens in 64 to be 10 ones. 4 ones plus these new 10 ones make 14 ones. We draw a magnifying glass around the top number to help children focus on the regrouping. 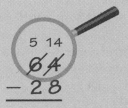 **Step 2** Subtract to find the answer. Children may subtract from left to right or from right to left. 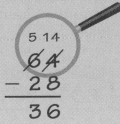

In explaining any method they use, children are expected to use "tens and ones" language. This shows that they understand they are subtracting 2 tens from 5 tens (not 2 from 5) and 8 ones from 14 ones.

Please call if you have any questions or comments.

Sincerely,
Your child's teacher

COMMON CORE

Unit 4 includes the Common Core Standards for Mathematical Content for Operations and Algebraic Thinking, 2.OA.1, 2.OA.2; Number and Operations in Base Ten, 2.NBT.4, 2.NBT.5, 2.NBT.6, 2.NBT.7, 2.NBT.8, 2.NBT.9; Measurement and Data, 2.MD.8; and all Mathematical Practices.

Estimada familia:

En este programa, los niños aprenden estos dos métodos para restar con números de 2 dígitos. Sin embargo, pueden usar cualquier método que comprendan, puedan explicar y puedan hacer relativamente rápido.

Método extendido	Método de desagrupar primero

Método extendido

Paso 1 "Extender" cada número para mostrar que consta de decenas y unidades.

$$64 = 60 + 4$$
$$-28 = 20 + 8$$

Paso 2 Observar si hay suficientes unidades para restar. Si no las hay, desagrupar una decena para formar 10 unidades y sumarla a las unidades existentes.

$$64 = \overset{50}{\cancel{60}} + \overset{14}{\cancel{4}}$$
$$-28 = 20 + 8$$

Paso 3 Restar para hallar la respuesta. Los niños pueden restar de izquierda a derecha o de derecha a izquierda.

$$64 = \overset{50}{\cancel{60}} + \overset{14}{\cancel{4}}$$
$$-28 = 20 + 8$$
$$30 + 6 = 36$$

Método de desagrupar primero

Paso 1 Observar si hay suficientes unidades para restar. Si no las hay, desagrupar una de las 6 decenas en 64 para obtener 10 unidades. 4 unidades más las 10 unidades nuevas son 14 unidades. Dibujamos una lupa alrededor del número superior para ayudar a los niños a concentrarse en desagrupar.

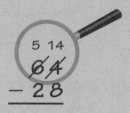

Paso 2 Restar para hallar la respuesta. Los niños pueden restar de izquierda a derecha o de derecha a izquierda.

Cuando los niños expliquen el método que usan, deben hacerlo usando un lenguaje relacionado con "decenas y unidades". Esto demuestra que comprenden que están restando 2 decenas de 5 decenas (no 2 de 5) y 8 unidades de 14 unidades.

Si tiene alguna duda o algún comentario, por favor comuníquese conmigo.

Atentamente,
El maestro de su niño

La Unidad 4 incluye los Common Core Standards for Mathematical Content for Operations and Algebraic Thinking, 2.OA.1, 2.OA.2; Number and Operations in Base Ten, 2.NBT.4, 2.NBT.5, 2.NBT.6, 2.NBT.7, 2.NBT.8, 2.NBT.9; Measurement and Data, 2.MD.8; and all Mathematical Practices.

Dear Family:

Your child is beginning a new unit on time.

You can help your child link the time concepts learned in school with the real world.

Together, look for clocks in your home. You might search for watches, alarm clocks, digital clocks, and clocks on appliances.

Talk about time throughout your family's day. For example, you can point to the clock during breakfast and say, "We usually eat breakfast at this time. It is 7:30 A.M."

In this unit, your child will learn to tell time to the hour, half hour, and five minutes. Your child will practice writing the time.

If you have any questions or comments, please call or write to me. Thank you.

Sincerely,
Your child's teacher

Unit 5 includes the Common Core Standards for Mathematical Content for Operations and Algebraic Thinking, 2.OA.1, 2.OA.2; Number and Operations in Base Ten, 2.NBT.2, 2.NBT.5; Measurement and Data, 2.MD.7, 2.MD.10; Geometry, 2.G.3 and all Mathematical Practices.

Estimada familia:

Su niño está empezando una unidad donde aprenderá sobre la hora.

Usted puede ayudarlo a que conecte los conceptos relacionados con la hora que aprendió en la escuela, con el mundo real.

Busquen juntos relojes en la casa. Puede buscar relojes de pulsera, relojes con alarma, relojes digitales y relojes que estén en los electrodomésticos.

Durante un día en familia, hablen de la hora. Por ejemplo, puede señalar un reloj durante el desayuno y decir: "Generalmente desayunamos a esta hora. Son las 7:30 a.m."

En esta unidad su niño aprenderá a leer la hora en punto, la media hora y los cinco minutos para la hora. Su niño practicará cómo escribir la hora.

Si tiene alguna pregunta o algún comentario, por favor comuníquese conmigo. Gracias.

Atentamente,
El maestro de su niño

COMMON CORE

La Unidad 5 incluye los Common Core Standards for Mathematical Content for Operations and Algebraic Thinking, 2.OA.1, 2.OA.2; Number and Operations in Base Ten, 2.NBT.2, 2.NBT.5; Measurement and Data, 2.MD.7, 2.MD.10; Geometry, 2.G.3 and all Mathematical Practices.

Dear Family:

Your child is learning how to show information in various ways. In this unit, children will learn how to create and read picture graphs and bar graphs.

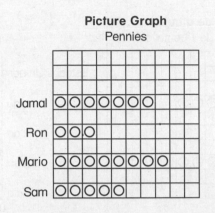

Picture Graph
Pennies

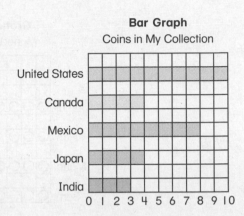

Bar Graph
Coins in My Collection

An important feature of *Math Expressions* is its emphasis on real world connections. Children will collect and represent data on graphs. They will also interpret the graph to answer questions about the data shown.

Children also explore the language of comparison by using such words as *same, more, less,* and *fewer*. The connection between pairs of terms is emphasized. For example: Carlos has 8 stickers. Maria has 3. Carlos has 5 *more* stickers than Maria. Maria has 5 *fewer* stickers than Carlos has.

Please call if you have any questions or concerns. Thank you for helping your child learn how to create, read, and interpret graphs.

Sincerely,
Your child's teacher

COMMON CORE Unit 5 includes the Common Core Standards for Mathematical Content for Operations and Algebraic Thinking, 2.OA.1, 2.OA.2; Number and Operations in Base Ten, 2.NBT.2, 2.NBT.5; Measurement and Data, 2.MD.7, 2.MD.10; Geometry, 2.G.3 and all Mathematical Practices.

Carta a la familia

Estimada familia:

Su niño está aprendiendo a mostrar información de varias maneras. En esta unidad los niños aprenderán a crear y a leer gráficas de dibujos y gráficas de barras.

Gráfica de dibujos
Monedas de 1 centavo

Jamal O O O O O O
Ron   O O O
Mario O O O O O O O
Sam   O O O O

Gráfica de barras
Monedas de mi colección

Estados Unidos
Canadá
México
Japón
India
0 1 2 3 4 5 6 7 8 9 10

Un aspecto importante de *Math Expressions* es su énfasis en las conexiones con situaciones de la vida cotidiana. Los niños reunirán datos y los representarán en gráficas. También interpretarán las gráficas para responder preguntas acerca de los datos que se muestran.

Los niños también estudiarán palabras que se usan para comparar, tales como *igual, mismo, más* y *menos*. Se hará énfasis en la conexión entre los pares de términos. Por ejemplo: Carlos tiene 8 adhesivos. María tiene 3. Carlos tiene 5 adhesivos *más* que María. María tiene 5 adhesivos *menos* que Carlos.

Si tiene alguna pregunta o algún comentario, por favor comuníquese conmigo. Gracias por ayudar a su niño a aprender cómo crear, leer e interpretar gráficas.

Atentamente,
El maestro de su niño

La Unidad 5 incluye los Common Core Standards for Mathematical Content for Operations and Algebraic Thinking, 2.OA.1, 2.OA.2; Number and Operations in Base Ten, 2.NBT.2, 2.NBT.5; Measurement and Data, 2.MD.7, 2.MD.10; Geometry, 2.G.3 and all Mathematical Practices.

Dear Family:

In this unit, children will learn how to add 3-digit numbers that have totals up to 1,000.

Children begin the unit by learning to count to 1,000. They count by ones from a number, over the hundred, and into the next hundred. For example, 498, 499, 500, 501, 502, 503. You can help your child practice counting aloud to 1,000. Listen carefully as he or she crosses over the hundred.

Children will learn to write numbers to 1,000. Some children will write 5003 instead of 503 for five hundred three. Using Secret Code Cards will help children write the numbers correctly.

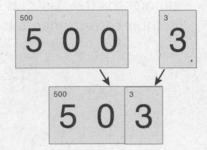

Help your child count small objects by making groups of 10 and then groups of 100. When the groups are made, help your child write the number of objects. This is a good way to help children recognize the difference between 5,003 and 503.

Please call if you have any questions or concerns. Thank you for helping your child learn about numbers to 1,000.

Sincerely,
Your child's teacher

Unit 6 includes the Common Core Standards for Mathematical Content for Operations and Algebraic Thinking 2.OA.1, Number and Operations in Base Ten 2.NBT.1, 2.NBT.1a, 2.NBT.1b, 2.NBT.2, 2.NBT.3, 2.NBT.4, 2.NBT.5, 2.NBT.7, 2.NBT.8, 2.NBT.9, Measurement and Data 2.MD.8, and all Mathematical Practices.

 COMMON CORE

Estimada familia:

En esta unidad los niños aprenderán cómo sumar números de 3 dígitos con totales de hasta 1,000.

Los niños comienzan la unidad aprendiendo a contar hasta 1,000. Cuentan de uno en uno a partir de un número, llegan a la centena y comienzan con la siguiente centena. Por ejemplo, 498, 499, 500, 501, 502, 503. Puede ayudar a su niño a practicar, contando en voz alta hasta 1,000. Ponga atención cada vez que llegue a una nueva centena.

Los niños aprenderán a escribir los números hasta 1,000. Tal vez, algunos niños escriban 5003 en vez de 503 al intentar escribir quinientos tres. Usar las Tarjetas de código secreto los ayudará a escribir correctamente los números.

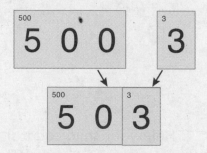

Ayude a su niño a contar objetos pequeños formando grupos de 10 y luego, grupos de 100. Cuando formen los grupos, ayúdelo a escribir el número de objetos. Esta es una buena manera de ayudar a los niños a reconocer la diferencia entre 5,003 y 503.

Si tiene alguna duda o pregunta, por favor comuníquese conmigo. Gracias por ayudar a su niño a aprender a contar hasta 1,000.

Atentamente,
El maestro de su niño

La Unidad 6 incluye los Common Core Standards for Mathematical Content for Operations and Algebraic Thinking 2.OA.1, Number and Operations in Base Ten 2.NBT.1, 2.NBT.1a, 2.NBT.1b, 2.NBT.2, 2.NBT.3, 2.NBT.4, 2.NBT.5, 2.NBT.7, 2.NBT.8, 2.NBT.9, Measurement and Data 2.MD.8, and all Mathematical Practices.

Family Letter

Dear Family:

Your child is now learning how to add 3-digit numbers. The methods children use are similar to those used for adding 2-digit numbers.

New Groups Below

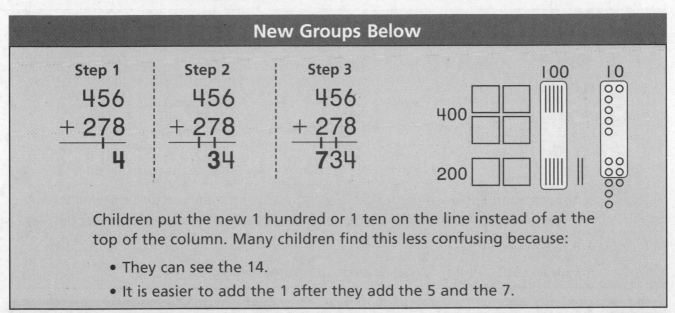

Children put the new 1 hundred or 1 ten on the line instead of at the top of the column. Many children find this less confusing because:

- They can see the 14.
- It is easier to add the 1 after they add the 5 and the 7.

Show All Totals

$$
\begin{array}{r}
456 \\
+\,278 \\
\hline
\end{array}
$$

hundreds → 600
tens → 120
ones → 14
734

Children see the hundreds, tens, and ones they are adding. These also can be seen when they make a math drawing like the one above.

Children may use any method that they understand, can explain, and can do fairly quickly. They should use hundreds, tens, and ones language to explain. This shows that they understand that they are adding 4 hundreds and 2 hundreds and not 4 and 2.

Please call if you have questions or comments.

Sincerely,
Your child's teacher

COMMON CORE

Unit 6 includes the Common Core Standards for Mathematical Content for Operations and Algebraic Thinking 2.OA.1, Number and Operations in Base Ten 2.NBT.1, 2.NBT.1a, 2.NBT.1b, 2.NBT.2, 2.NBT.3, 2.NBT.4, 2.NBT.5, 2.NBT.7, 2.NBT.8, 2.NBT.9, Measurement and Data 2.MD.8, and all Mathematical Practices.

Estimada familia:

Ahora su niño está aprendiendo a sumar números de 3 dígitos. Los métodos que los niños usarán son semejantes a los usados para sumar numeros de 2 dígitos.

Grupos nuevos abajo

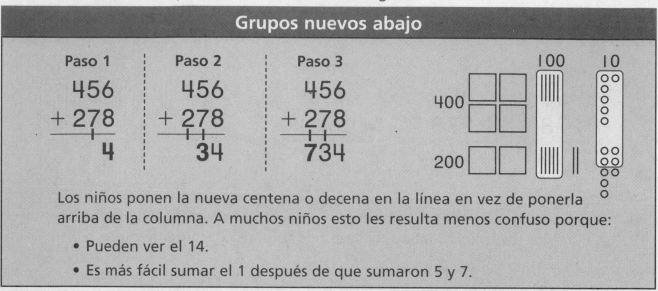

Paso 1
$$\begin{array}{r} 456 \\ +278 \\ \hline 4 \end{array}$$

Paso 2
$$\begin{array}{r} 456 \\ +278 \\ \hline 34 \end{array}$$

Paso 3
$$\begin{array}{r} 456 \\ +278 \\ \hline 734 \end{array}$$

100   10

400

200

Los niños ponen la nueva centena o decena en la línea en vez de ponerla arriba de la columna. A muchos niños esto les resulta menos confuso porque:

• Pueden ver el 14.

• Es más fácil sumar el 1 después de que sumaron 5 y 7.

Mostrar todos los totales

$$\begin{array}{r} 456 \\ +278 \\ \end{array}$$

centenas → 600

decenas → 120

unidades → 14

734

Los niños ven las centenas, las decenas y las unidades que están sumando. Esto también se puede observar cuando hacen un dibujo matemático como el de arriba.

Los niños pueden usar cualquier método que comprendan, puedan explicar y puedan hacer relativamente rápido. Para explicar deben usar un lenguaje relacionado con centenas, decenas y unidades. Esto demuestra que entienden que están sumando 4 centenas y 2 centenas, y no 4 y 2.

Si tiene alguna duda o pregunta, por favor comuníquese conmigo.

Atentamente,
El maestro de su niño

COMMON CORE

La Unidad 6 incluye los Common Core Standards for Mathematical Content for Operations and Algebraic Thinking 2.OA.1, Number and Operations in Base Ten 2.NBT.1, 2.NBT.1a, 2.NBT.1b, 2.NBT.2, 2.NBT.3, 2.NBT.4, 2.NBT.5, 2.NBT.7, 2.NBT.8, 2.NBT.9, Measurement and Data 2.MD.8, and all Mathematical Practices.

Dear Family:

Your child is now learning how to subtract 3-digit numbers. The most important part is understanding and being able to explain a method. Children may use any method that they understand, can explain, and can perform fairly quickly.

Expanded Method

Step 1   Step 2

$$432 = 400 + 30 + 2$$
$$- 273 = 200 + 70 + 3$$

Step 2
$$= \begin{array}{c} 120 \\ 300 \quad 20 \quad 12 \\ 400 + 30 + 2 \\ 200 + 70 + 3 \end{array}$$

Step 3 $\begin{cases} 100 + 50 + 9 \\ = 159 \end{cases}$

Step 1 "Expand" each number to show that it is made up of hundreds, tens, and ones.

Step 2 Check to see if there are enough ones to subtract from. If not, ungroup a ten into 10 ones and add it to the existing ones. Check to see if there are enough tens to subtract from. If not, ungroup a hundred into 10 tens and add it to the existing tens. Children may also ungroup from the left.

Step 3 Subtract to find the answer. Children may subtract from left to right or right to left.

Ungroup First Method

Step 1 Check to see if there are enough ones and tens to subtract from. Ungroup where needed.

Look inside 432. Ungroup 432 and rename it as 3 hundreds, 12 tens, and 12 ones.

Ungroup from the left: **Ungroup from the right:**

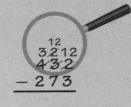

Step 2 Subtract to find the answer. Children may subtract from the left or from the right.

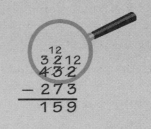

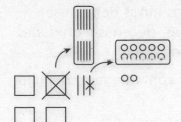

In explaining any method they use, children are expected to use "hundreds, tens, and ones" language and drawings to show that they understand place value.

Please call if you have questions or comments.

Sincerely,
Your child's teacher

COMMON CORE

Unit 6 includes the Common Core Standards for Mathematical Content for Operations and Algebraic Thinking 2.OA.1, Number and Operations in Base Ten 2.NBT.1, 2.NBT.1a, 2.NBT.1b, 2.NBT.2, 2.NBT.3, 2.NBT.4, 2.NBT.7, 2.NBT.8, 2.NBT.9, Measurement and Data 2.MD.8, and all Mathematical Practices.

Carta a la familia

Estimada familia:

Su niño está aprendiendo a restar números de 3 dígitos. Lo más importante es comprender y saber explicar un método. Los niños pueden usar cualquier método que comprendan, puedan explicar y puedan hacer relativamente rápido.

Método extendido

Paso·1   Paso 2

$$
\begin{array}{l}
\quad\quad\quad\quad\quad\quad\quad\quad 120 \\
\quad\quad\quad\quad\quad\quad 300 \quad 20 \quad 12 \\
432 = 400 + 30 + 2 = 400 + 30 + 2 \\
-273 = 200 + 70 + 3 = 200 + 70 + 3
\end{array}
$$

$$
\text{Paso 3} \begin{cases} 100 + 50 + 9 \\ = 159 \end{cases}
$$

Paso 1 "Extender" cada número para mostrar que consta de centenas, decenas y unidades.

Paso 2 Observar si hay suficientes unidades para restar. Si no, desagrupar una decena para formar 10 unidades y sumarlas a las unidades existentes. Observar si hay suficientes decenas para restar. Si no, desagrupar una centena para formar 10 decenas y sumarlas a las decenas existentes. Los niños también pueden desagrupar por la izquierda.

Paso 3 Restar para hallar la respuesta. Los niños pueden restar de izquierda a derecha o de derecha a izquierda.

Método de desagrupar primero

Paso 1 Observar si hay suficientes unidades y decenas para restar. Desagrupar cuando haga falta.

Mirar dentro de 432. Desagrupar 432 y volver a nombrarlo como 3 centenas, 12 decenas y 12 unidades.

Desagrupar por la izquierda: **Desagrupar por la derecha:**

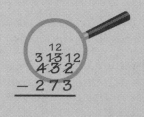   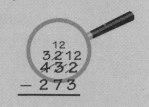

Paso 2 Restar para hallar la respuesta. Los niños pueden restar empezando por la izquierda o por la derecha.

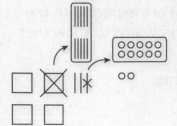

Para explicar cualquier método que usen, los niños deben usar lenguaje y dibujos relacionados con centenas, decenas y unidades para demostrar que comprenden el valor posicional.

Si tiene alguna duda o comentario, por favor comuníquese conmigo.

Atentamente,
El maestro de su niño

COMMON CORE

La Unidad 6 incluye los Common Core Standards for Mathematical Content for Operations and Algebraic Thinking 2.OA.1, Number and Operations in Base Ten 2.NBT.1, 2.NBT.1a, 2.NBT.1b, 2.NBT.2, 2.NBT.3, 2.NBT.4, 2.NBT.7, 2.NBT.8, 2.NBT.9, Measurement and Data 2.MD.8, and all Mathematical Practices.

Family Letter

Dear Family:

In this unit, your child will learn about rectangular arrays and how to use addition to count the number of objects in an array. The array below has 2 rows and 3 columns. It can be described as 2 rows with 3 tiles in each row or 3 columns with 2 tiles in each column.

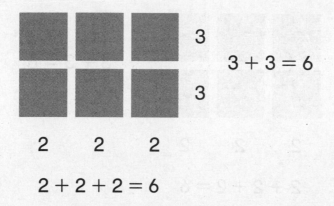

You can help your child by working with him or her to practice using the words *array*, *rows*, and *columns*. For example, ask your child to use pennies or other small objects to make an array that has 4 rows with 5 objects in each row. Ask your child to write the addition equations that show the total number of objects in the array. ($5 + 5 + 5 + 5 = 20$ and $4 + 4 + 4 + 4 + 4 = 20$)

Your child will also be learning about equal parts of circles and rectangles: 2 *halves*, 3 *thirds*, and 4 *fourths*. You can practice using this vocabulary at home. For example, "I am cutting this pizza into 4 fourths."

Please call if you have any questions or concerns.

Sincerely,
Your child's teacher

COMMON CORE

Unit 7 includes the Common Core Standards for Mathematical Content for Operations and Algebraic Thinking 2.OA.1, 2.OA.3, 2.OA.4, Geometry 2.G.1, 2.G.2, 2.G.3, Measurement and Data 2.MD.5, 2.MD.6, and all Mathematical Practices.

Estimada familia:

En esta unidad, su niño aprenderá acerca de las matrices rectangulares y aprenderá cómo usar la suma para contar el número de objetos en una matriz. La matriz de abajo tiene 2 hileras y 3 columnas. Puede describirse así: 2 hileras con 3 fichas en cada columna, o 3 columnas con 2 fichas en cada columna.

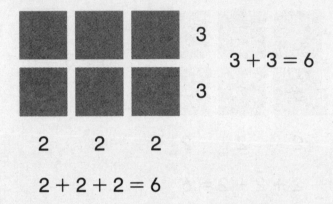

$$3 + 3 = 6$$

$$2 + 2 + 2 = 6$$

Usted puede ayudar a su niño practicando el uso de las palabras *matriz, hileras* y *columnas*. Por ejemplo, pídale que use monedas de un centavo u otros objetos pequeños para hacer una matriz que tenga 4 hileras con 5 objetos en cada una. Pida a su niño que escriba la ecuación de suma que muestra el número total de objetos en la matriz. ($5 + 5 + 5 + 5 = 20$ y $4 + 4 + 4 + 4 + 4 = 20$)

Su niño también aprenderá acerca de partes iguales de círculos y rectángulos: 2 *medios,* 3 *tercios* y 4 *cuartos.* Pueden practicar usando este vocabulario en casa. Por ejemplo: "Estoy cortando esta pizza en 4 cuartos".

Si tiene alguna duda o algún comentario, por favor comuníquese conmigo.

Atentamente,
El maestro de su niño

COMMON CORE La Unidad 7 incluye los Common Core Standards for Mathematical Content for Operations and Algebraic Thinking 2.OA.1, 2.OA.3, 2.OA.4, Geometry 2.G.1, 2.G.2, 2.G.3, Measurement and Data 2.MD.5, 2.MD.6, and all Mathematical Practices.

0 + 1 0 + 3 0 + 5
0   2   4   6

I   E   S

0 + 0 0 + 2 0 + 4 0 + 6

0 + L 0 + 9 I + Z 4 + h

8   2   4

L   9   E   S

0 + 8 I + I I + 3

I + 9 I + 8 2 + 2

6   8   01   5

L   9   h

1 + 5 1 + 7 1 + 9 3 + 2

h + Z 9 + Z 8 + Z E + E

7   9   10

9   8   01   9

5 + 2 7 + 2 5 + 5

5 + 3   7 + 3   4 + 3   5 + 3
7   9   10   8

8   10   9
4 + 3   6 + 3   4 + 6   4 + 4

9 + 3   4 + 7   9 + 6   5 + 9
11   12   11

12   11   13   11
8 + 3   4 + 8   9 + 2

5 + 8   9 + 9   8 + 9
12   14   13   15

13   12   14
5 + 7   5 + 9   7 + 6   9 + 6

7 + 7   6 + 7   9 + 8
15   16   18

14   16   17
8 + 7   8 + 8   9 + 9

$5 + 7 = \boxed{}$ $6 + 7 = \boxed{}$ $9 + 9 = \boxed{}$

$8 + 7 = \boxed{}$ $9 + 7 = \boxed{}$ $3 + 8 = \boxed{}$

$4 + 8 = \boxed{}$ $5 + 8 = \boxed{}$ $6 + 8 = \boxed{}$

$7 + 8 = \boxed{}$ $8 + 8 = \boxed{}$ $9 + 8 = \boxed{}$

$3 + 9 = \boxed{}$ $4 + 9 = \boxed{}$ $5 + 9 = \boxed{}$

Green Make-a-Ten Cards (front)
*Copy on green cardstock.

$9 + 9 = \boxed{18}$

9 • | • • • •

9 + 1 + 8

$6 + 7 = \boxed{13}$

7 | • • • | • • •

7 + 3 + 3

$5 + 7 = \boxed{12}$

7 | • • • | • •

7 + 3 + 2

$3 + 8 = \boxed{11}$

8 | • • | •

8 + 2 + 1

$9 + 7 = \boxed{16}$

9 | • | • • • • •

9 + 1 + 6

$8 + 7 = \boxed{15}$

8 | • • | • • • • •

8 + 2 + 5

$6 + 8 = \boxed{14}$

8 | • • | • • • •

8 + 2 + 4

$5 + 8 = \boxed{13}$

8 | • • | • • •

8 + 2 + 3

$4 + 8 = \boxed{12}$

8 | • • | • •

8 + 2 + 2

$9 + 8 = \boxed{17}$

9 | • | • • • •

9 + 1 + 7

$8 + 8 = \boxed{16}$

8 | • • | • • • • • •

8 + 2 + 6

$7 + 8 = \boxed{15}$

8 | • • | • • • • •

8 + 2 + 5

$5 + 9 = \boxed{14}$

9 | • | • • • •

9 + 1 + 4

$4 + 9 = \boxed{13}$

9 | • | • • •

9 + 1 + 3

$3 + 9 = \boxed{12}$

9 | • | • •

9 + 1 + 2

$6 + 9 = \boxed{}$

$7 + 9 = \boxed{}$

$7 + 4 = \boxed{}$

$8 + 4 = \boxed{}$

$9 + 4 = \boxed{}$

$6 + 5 = \boxed{}$

$7 + 5 = \boxed{}$

$8 + 5 = \boxed{}$

$9 + 5 = \boxed{}$

$5 + 6 = \boxed{}$

$8 + 9 = \boxed{}$

$7 + 6 = \boxed{}$

$8 + 6 = \boxed{}$

$9 + 6 = \boxed{}$

$4 + 7 = \boxed{}$

Green Make-a-Ten Cards (front)
*Copy on green cardstock.

$7 + 4 = \boxed{11}$

| 7 | ••• • |

7 + 3 + 1

$7 + 9 = \boxed{16}$

| 9 | • | ••••• |

9 + 1 + 6

$6 + 9 = \boxed{15}$

| 9 | • | ••••• |

9 + 1 + 5

$6 + 5 = \boxed{11}$

| 6 | ••••• • |

6 + 4 + 1

$9 + 4 = \boxed{13}$

| 9 | • | ••• |

9 + 1 + 3

$8 + 4 = \boxed{12}$

| 8 | •• | •• |

8 + 2 + 2

$9 + 5 = \boxed{14}$

| 9 | • | •••• |

9 + 1 + 4

$8 + 5 = \boxed{13}$

| 8 | •• | ••• |

8 + 2 + 3

$7 + 5 = \boxed{12}$

| 7 | ••• | •• |

7 + 3 + 2

$7 + 6 = \boxed{13}$

| 7 | ••• | ••• |

7 + 3 + 3

$8 + 9 = \boxed{17}$

| 9 | • | ••••• ••• |

9 + 1 + 7

$5 + 6 = \boxed{11}$

| 6 | ••••• • |

6 + 4 + 1

$4 + 7 = \boxed{11}$

| 7 | ••• • |

7 + 3 + 1

$9 + 6 = \boxed{15}$

| 9 | • | ••••• |

9 + 1 + 5

$8 + 6 = \boxed{14}$

| 8 | •• | •••• |

8 + 2 + 4

$15 - 6 = \boxed{}$ $16 - 7 = \boxed{}$ $11 - 7 = \boxed{}$

$12 - 8 = \boxed{}$ $13 - 9 = \boxed{}$ $11 - 6 = \boxed{}$

$12 - 7 = \boxed{}$ $13 - 8 = \boxed{}$ $14 - 9 = \boxed{}$

$11 - 5 = \boxed{}$ $17 - 8 = \boxed{}$ $13 - 7 = \boxed{}$

$14 - 8 = \boxed{}$ $15 - 9 = \boxed{}$ $11 - 4 = \boxed{}$

Blue Make-a-Ten Cards (front)
*Copy on blue cardstock.

$$11 - 7 = 4$$
3
1

$$16 - 7 = 9$$
3
6

$$15 - 6 = 9$$
4
5

$$11 - 6 = 5$$
4
1

$$13 - 9 = 4$$
1
3

$$12 - 8 = 4$$
2
2

$$14 - 9 = 5$$
1
4

$$13 - 8 = 5$$
2
3

$$12 - 7 = 5$$
3
2

$$13 - 7 = 6$$
3
3

$$17 - 8 = 9$$
2
7

$$11 - 5 = 6$$
5
1

$$11 - 4 = 7$$
6
1

$$15 - 9 = 6$$
1
5

$$14 - 8 = 6$$
2
4

Math Expressions
© Houghton Mifflin Harcourt Publishing Company

M8

Blue Make-a-Ten Cards (back)
*Copy on blue cardstock.

$12 - 5 = \boxed{}$

$13 - 6 = \boxed{}$

$18 - 9 = \boxed{}$

$15 - 8 = \boxed{}$

$16 - 9 = \boxed{}$

$11 - 3 = \boxed{}$

$12 - 4 = \boxed{}$

$13 - 5 = \boxed{}$

$14 - 6 = \boxed{}$

$15 - 7 = \boxed{}$

$16 - 8 = \boxed{}$

$17 - 9 = \boxed{}$

$12 - 3 = \boxed{}$

$13 - 4 = \boxed{}$

$14 - 5 = \boxed{}$

Blue Make-a-Ten Cards (front)
*Copy on blue cardstock.

$18 - 9 = \boxed{9}$
1
8

$13 - 6 = \boxed{7}$
4
3

$12 - 5 = \boxed{7}$
5
2

$11 - 3 = \boxed{8}$
7
1

$16 - 9 = \boxed{7}$
1
6

$15 - 8 = \boxed{7}$
2
5

$14 - 6 = \boxed{8}$
4
4

$13 - 5 = \boxed{8}$
5
3

$12 - 4 = \boxed{8}$
6
2

$17 - 9 = \boxed{8}$
1
7

$16 - 8 = \boxed{8}$
2
6

$15 - 7 = \boxed{8}$
3
5

$14 - 5 = \boxed{9}$
5
4

$13 - 4 = \boxed{9}$
6
3

$12 - 3 = \boxed{9}$
7
2

Blue Make-a-Ten Cards (back)
*Copy on blue cardstock.

1	2	10	20
1	**2**	**1 0**	**2 0**

3	4	30	40
3	**4**	**3 0**	**4 0**

5	6	50	60
5	**6**	**5 0**	**6 0**

7	8	70	80
7	**8**	**7 0**	**8 0**

9	90	100
9	**9 0**	**1 0 0**

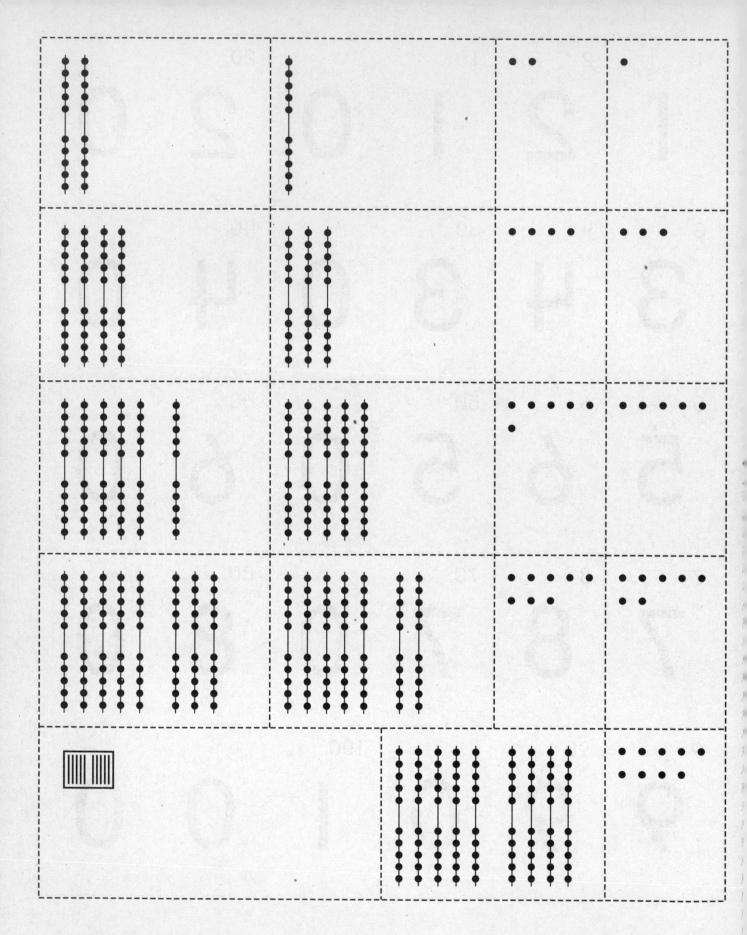

200

2 0 0

300

3 0 0

400

4 0 0

500

5 0 0

600

6 0 0

700

7 0 0

800

8 0 0

900

9 0 0

1000

1 0 0 0

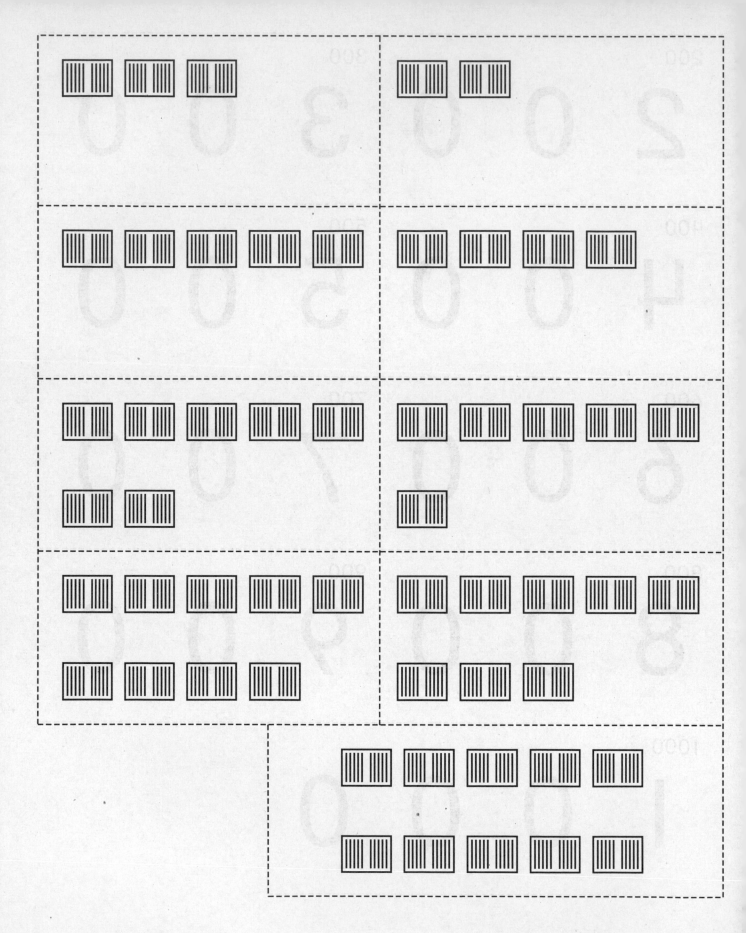

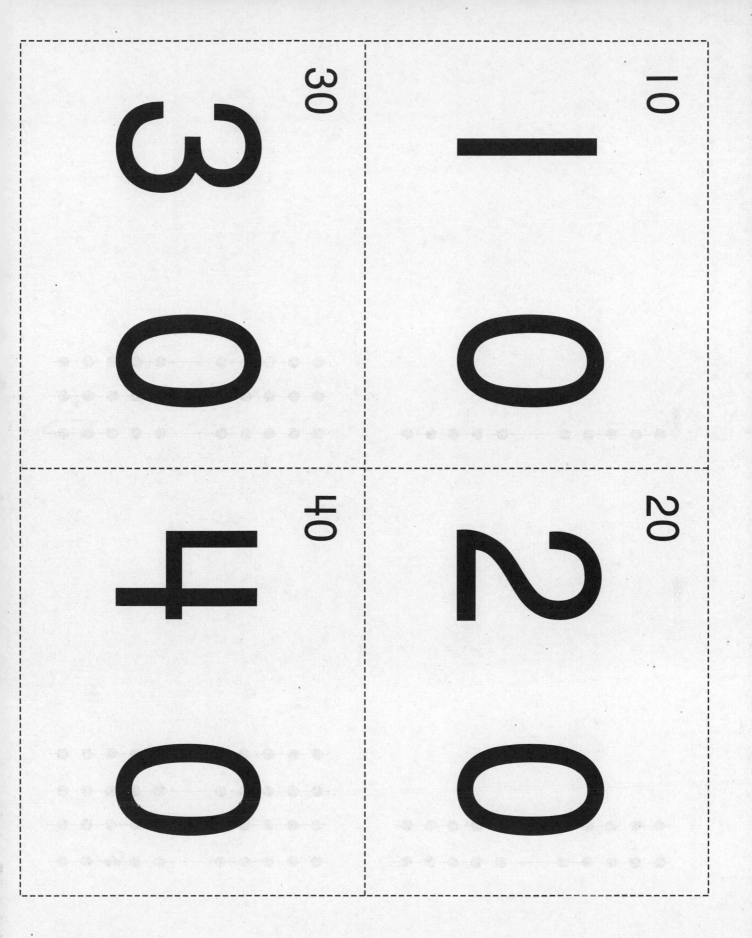

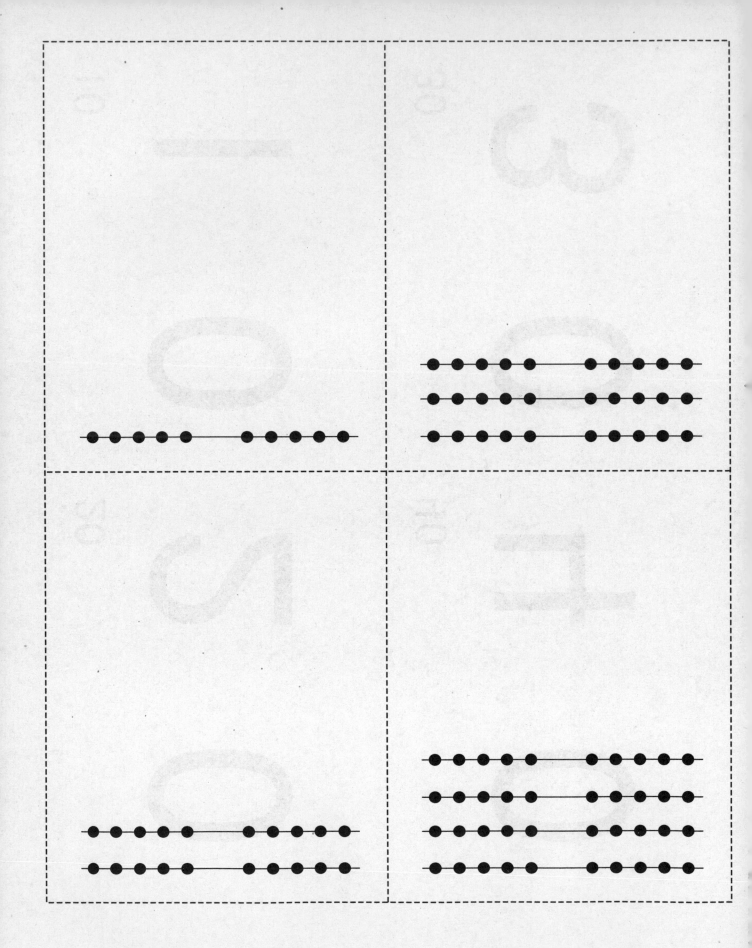

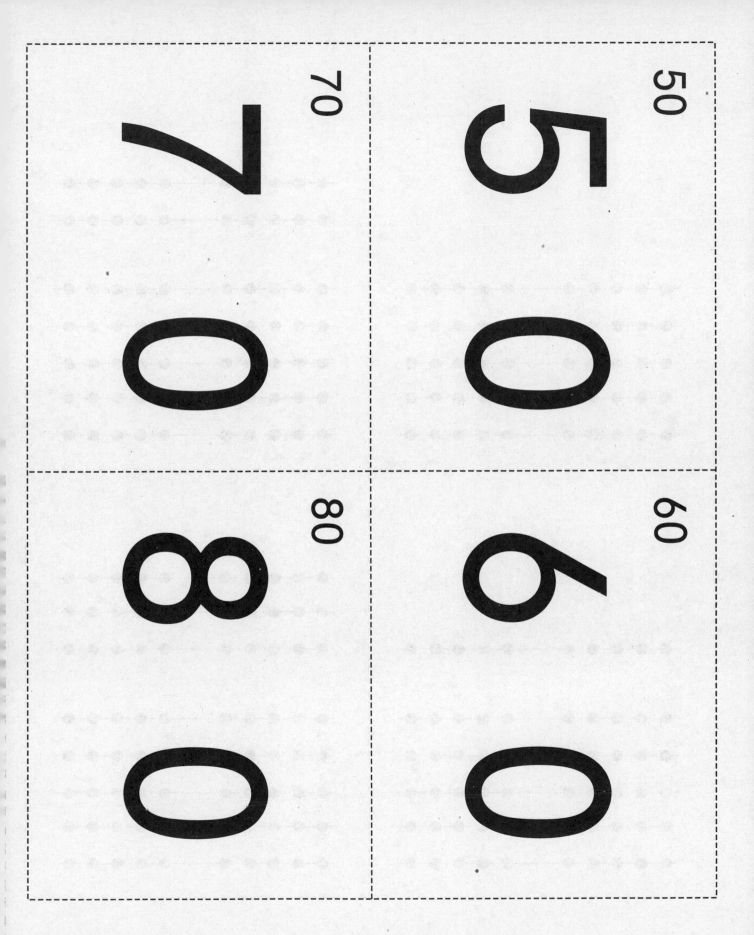

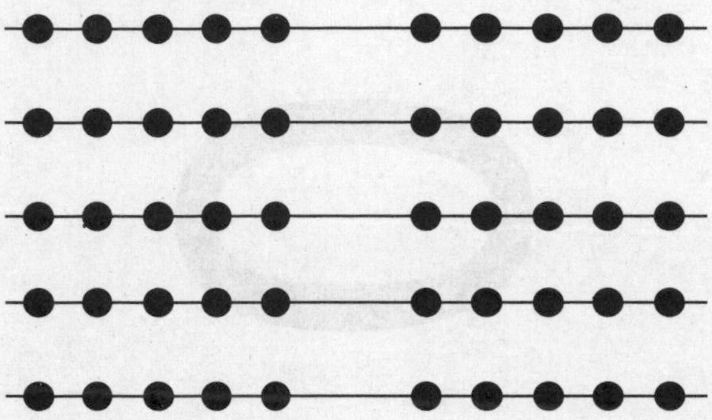

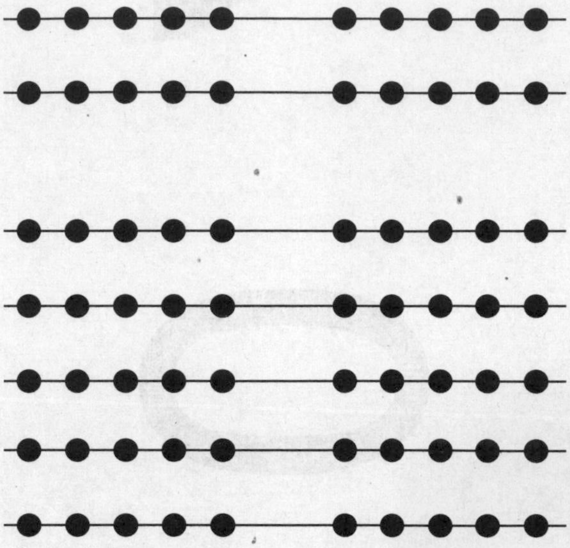

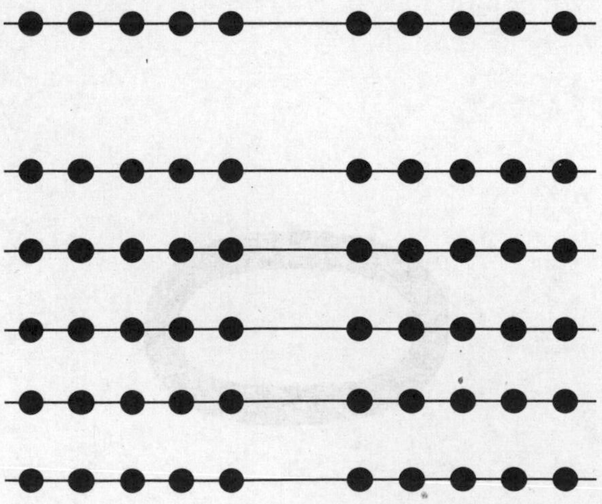

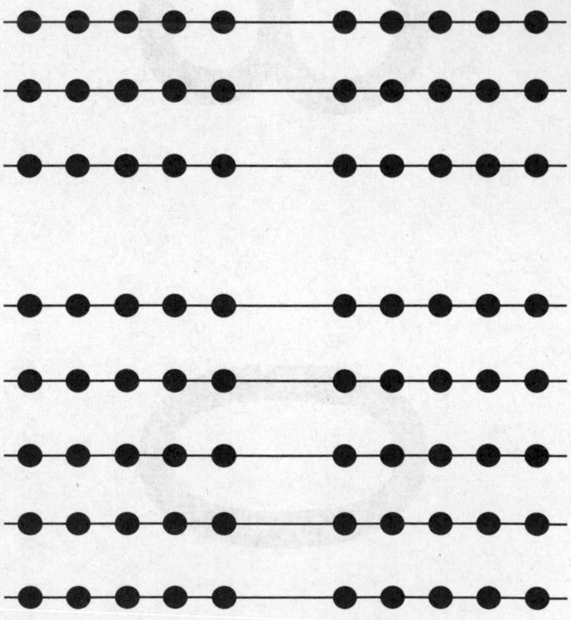

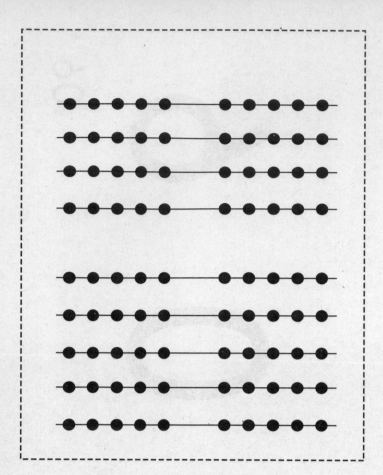

200

2 0 0

100

1 0 0

2

2

1

1

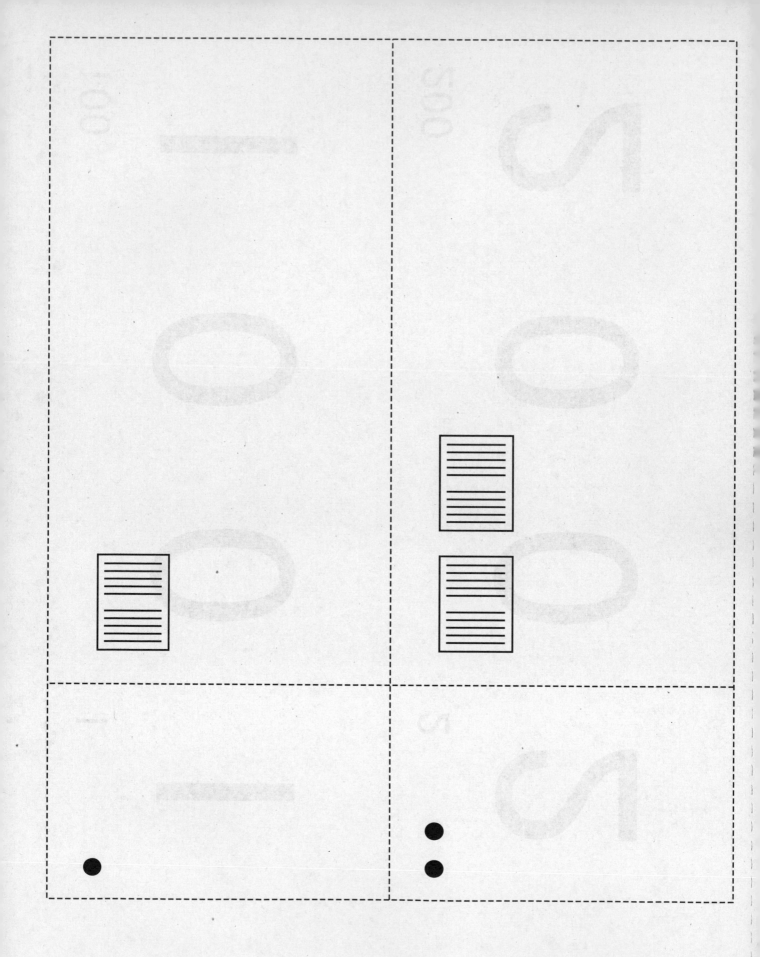

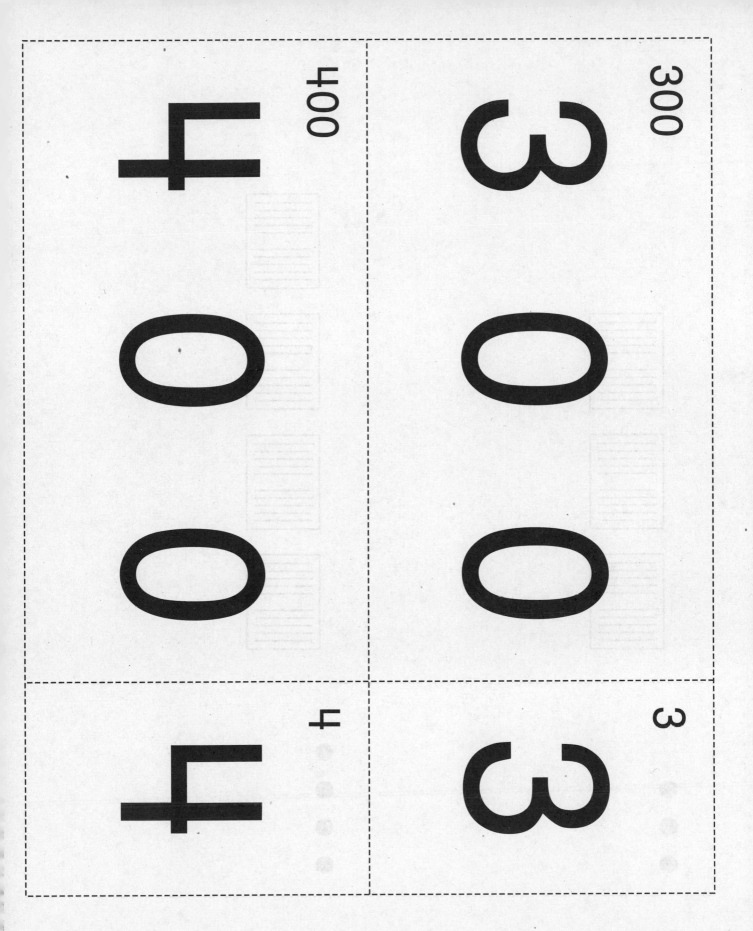

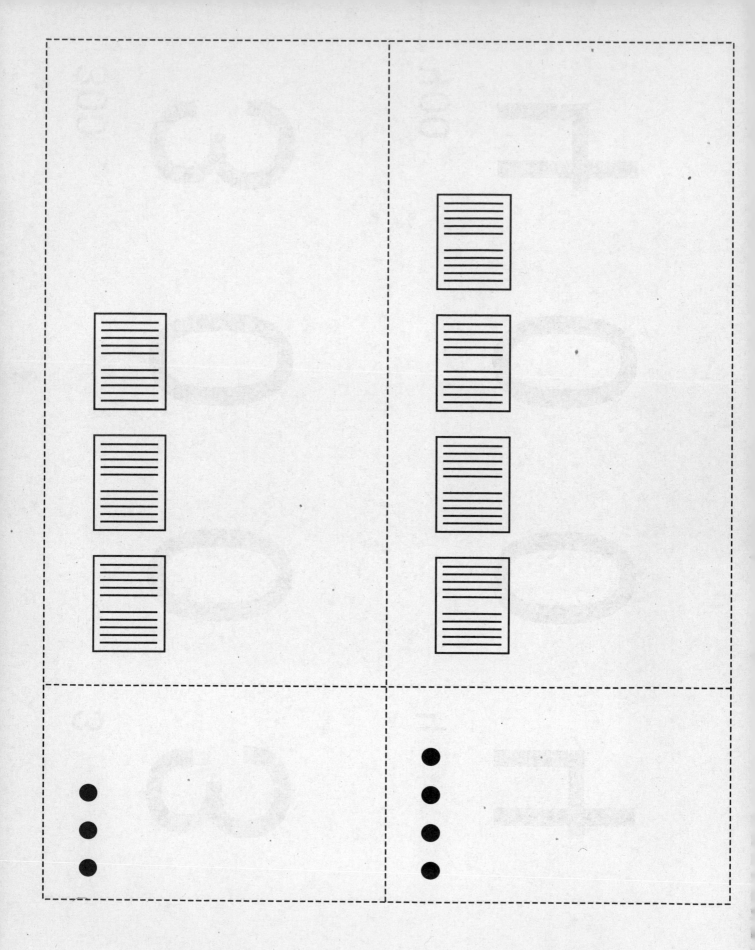

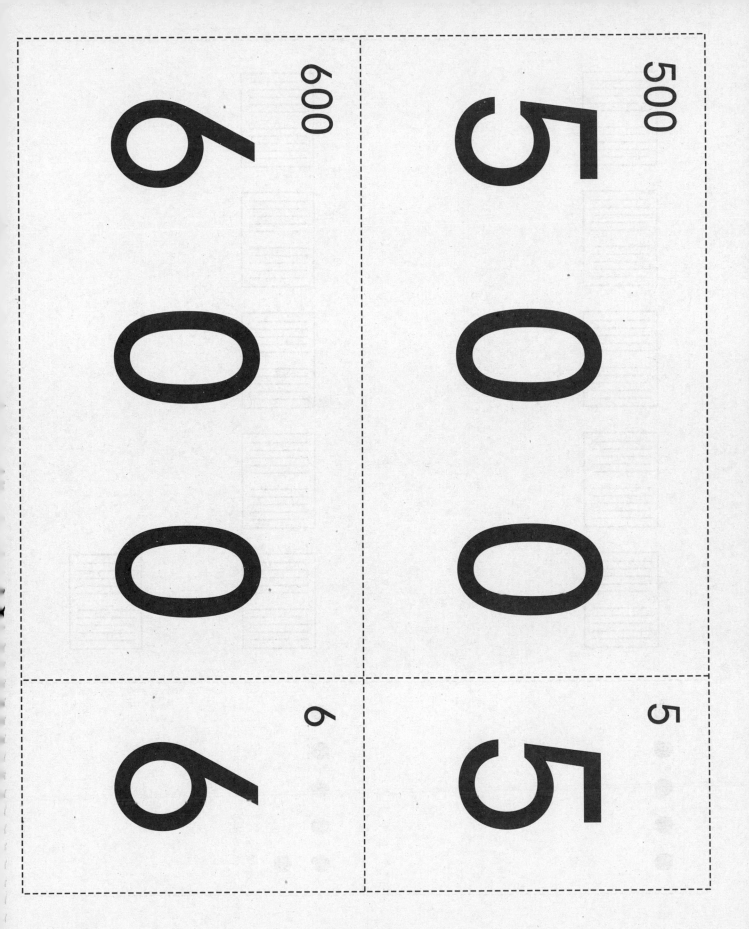

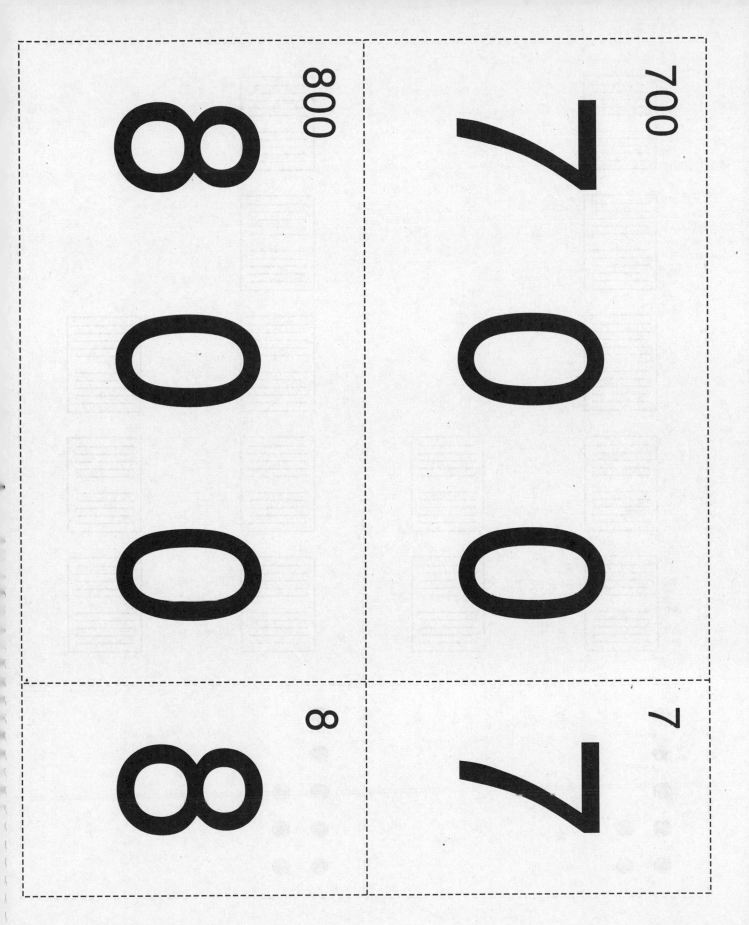

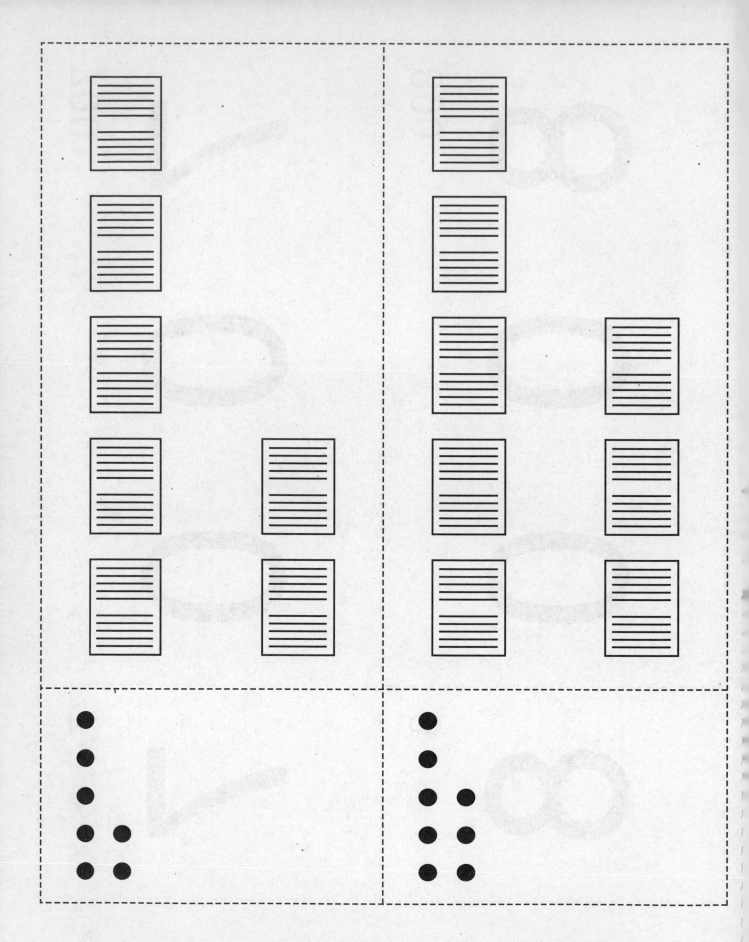

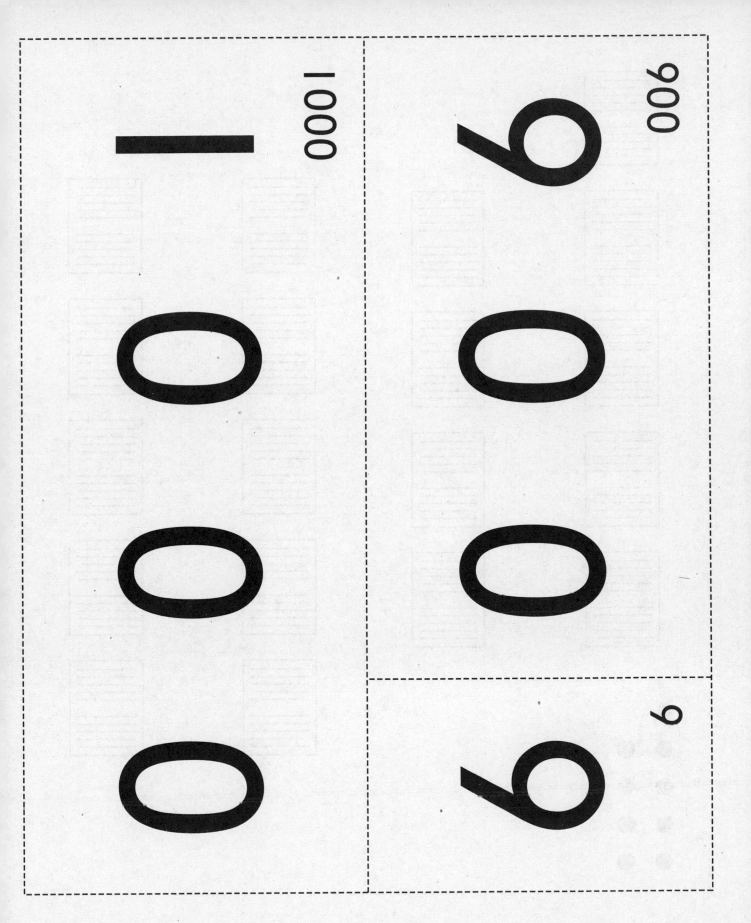

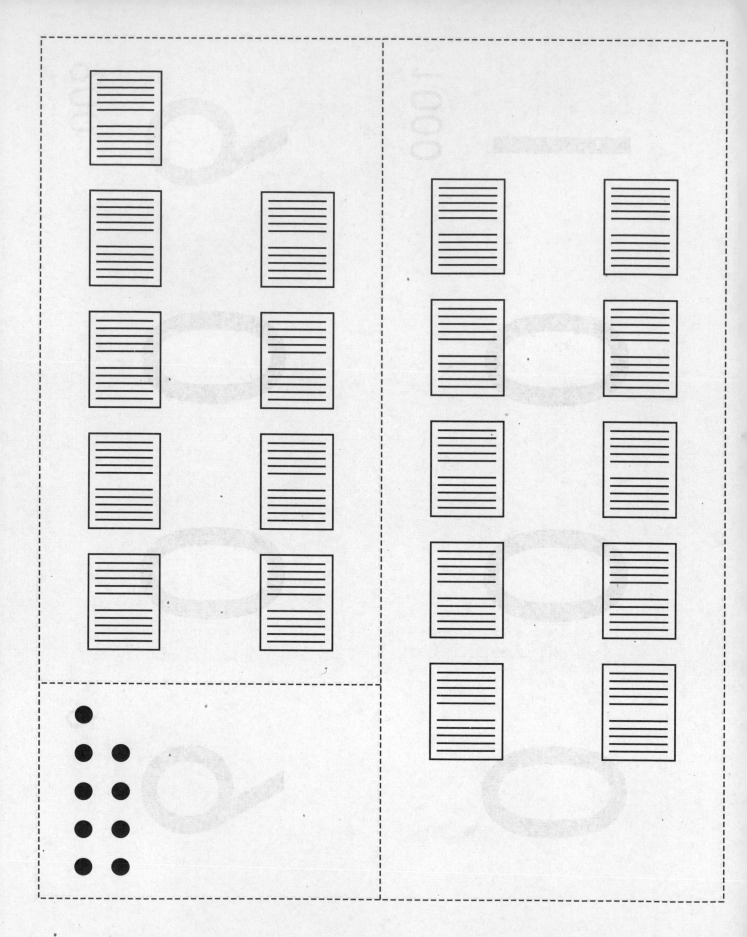

1	2	3	4	5	6	7	8	9	10
11	12	13	14	15	16	17	18	19	20
21	22	23	24	25	26	27	28	29	30
31	32	33	34	35	36	37	38	39	40
41	42	43	44	45	46	47	48	49	50
51	52	53	54	55	56	57	58	59	60
61	62	63	64	65	66	67	68	69	70
71	72	73	74	75	76	77	78	79	80
81	82	83	84	85	86	87	88	89	90
91	92	93	94	95	96	97	98	99	100
101	102	103	104	105	106	107	108	109	110
111	112	113	114	115	116	117	118	119	120

Math Expressions
© Houghton Mifflin Harcourt Publishing Company

M31

120 Poster (front)
This page can be enlarged to make a classroom poster.

121	122	123	124	125	126	127	128	129	130
131	132	133	134	135	136	137	138	139	140
141	142	143	144	145	146	147	148	149	150
151	152	153	154	155	156	157	158	159	160
161	162	163	164	165	166	167	168	169	170
171	172	173	174	175	176	177	178	179	180
181	182	183	184	185	186	187	188	189	190
191	192	193	194	195	196	197	198	199	200
201	202	203	204	205	206	207	208	209	210
211	212	213	214	215	216	217	218	219	220
221	222	223	224	225	226	227	228	229	230
231	232	233	234	235	236	237	238	239	240

This page can be enlarged to make a classroom poster.

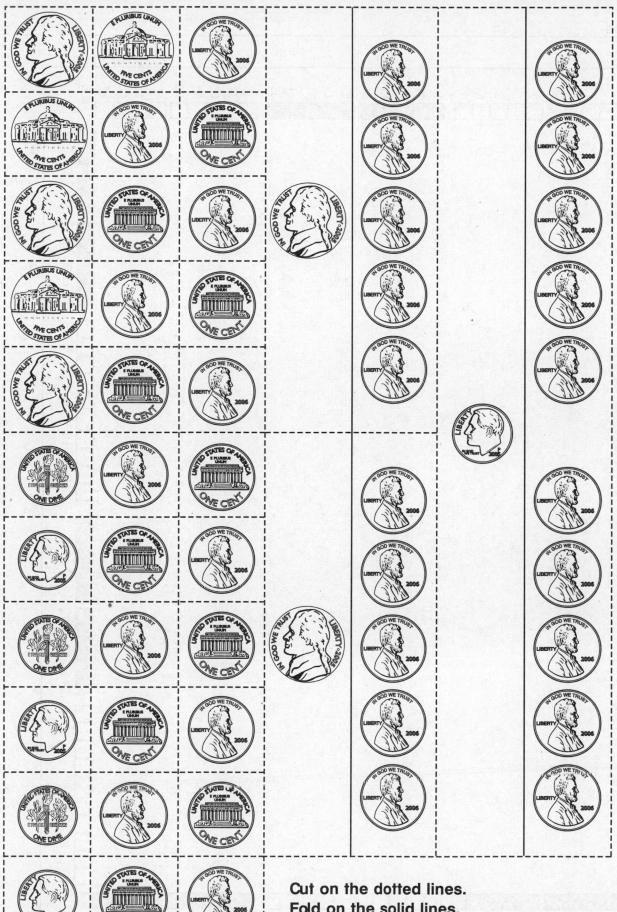

Cut on the dotted lines.
Fold on the solid lines.

M36

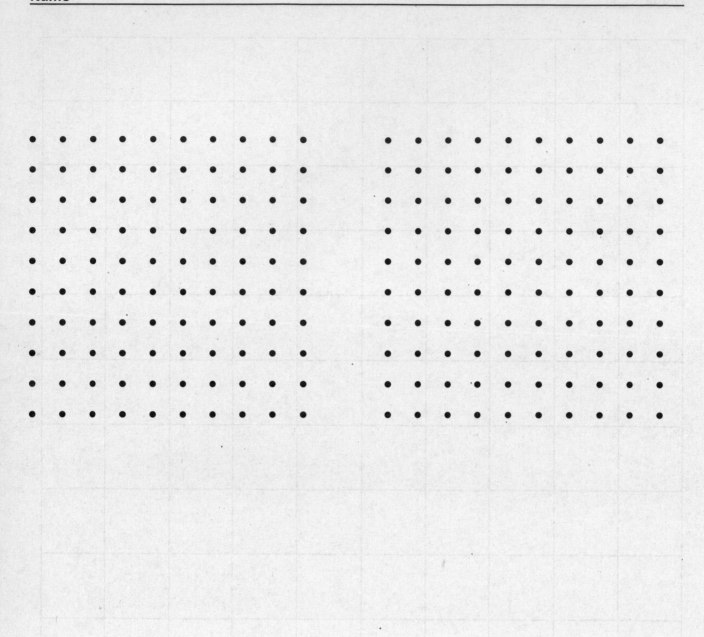

Attach the clock hands using a prong fastener.

5

0

6

1

7

2

8

3

9

4

There are 15 hidden equations. None have a + sign or = sign.
Ring as many as you can find. Add the + and = signs.

(8 + 7 = 15)	10	5	6	9	15
10	4	4	5	8	6	5	11
8	5	7	2	13	8	9	8
13	+	11	6	8	14	3	18
3	7 = 12	19	9	1	4	7	12
7	2	7	6	13	0	7	10
4	11	3	4	9	13	7	5
8	5	9	0	3	10	14	9
12	4	7	6	6	12	2	8
15	3	16	7	8	8	16	17

Lisa made the greatest number of bracelets possible.

She used the beads to make bracelets.

How many beads are left over?

Lisa had 83 beads.

Each bracelet had 10 beads.

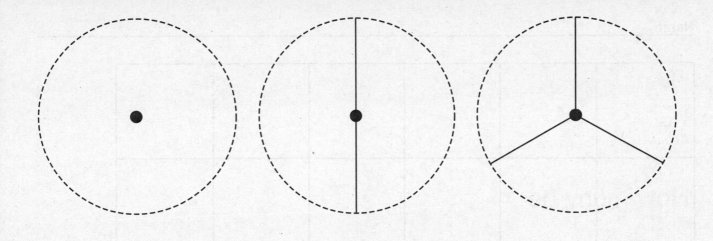

You can use a photocopy machine to enlarge individual spinners.

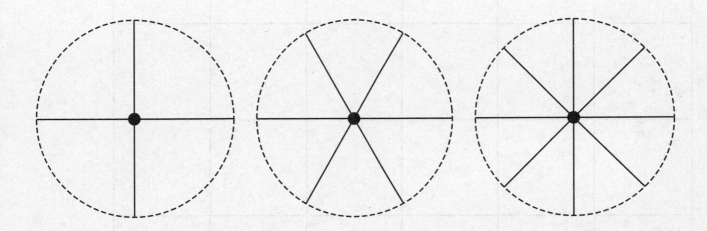

Two Ways to Make a Spinner

1. • Cut out a spinner from above.

   • Place a paper clip in the center of the spinner.

   • Place the pencil point in the center of the spinner and push the end of the paper clip so it rests behind the pencil point and spin!

2. • Cut out a spinner from above.

   • Open a paper clip so that it is an "L" shape.

   • Pierce the center of the spinner. Insert half of the clip under the spinner and the other half above. Keep the "L" shape.

   • Place another paper clip over the part sticking up. Spin!

Name

Name

Hundreds	Tens	Ones

+

Hundreds	Tens	Ones

+

Hundreds	Tens	Ones

+

Hundreds	Tens	Ones

+

Hundreds	Tens	Ones

−

Hundreds	Tens	Ones

−

Hundreds	Tens	Ones

−

Hundreds	Tens	Ones

−

Get 5 Dimes

1
2
3
4
5
6
7
8
9
10

11
12
13
14
15
16
17
18
19
20

21
22
23
24
25
26
27
28
29
30

31
32
33
34
35
36
37
38
39
40

41
42
43
44
45
46
47
48
49
50

Cut along the dashed lines.

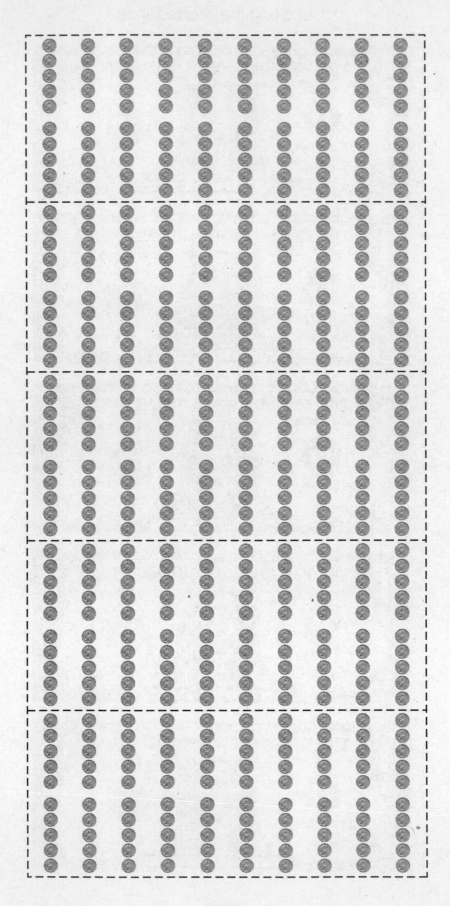

20¢	
12¢	
25¢	
4¢	
40¢	
16¢	

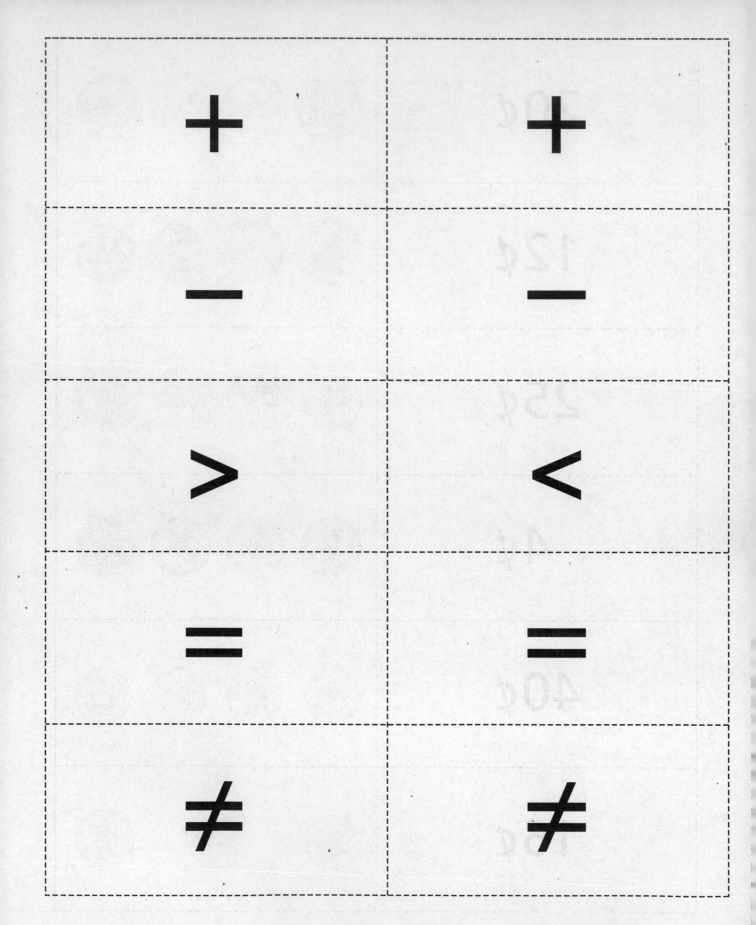

New Ten Challenge

Work in . Lay out Secret Code Cards like this.

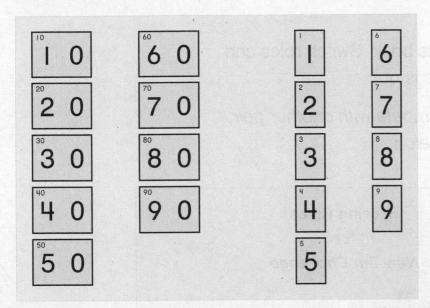

1. Use Secret Code Cards to help you make a 2-digit addition (sum less than 100).

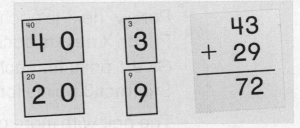

2. Make another 2-digit addition.

- Use the same tens cards.

- If *made a new ten,* use ones cards that *do not make a new ten.*

- If *did not make a new ten,* use ones cards that *make a new ten.*

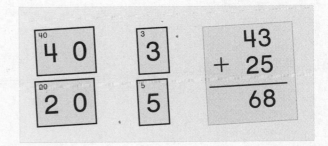

Activity continues on next page.

New Ten Challenge (continued)

2. 👥 Work together to check your work.
Correct any errors.

3. Put the Secret Code Cards back. Switch roles and
repeat. Continue until time is up.

*To play as a game and compete with another pair,
use the **Scoring Rules** below.*

**Scoring Rules
for
*New Ten Challenge***

· Trade papers with another pair.

· Put a ✓ next to each correct answer.
Put an X next to each incorrect answer.

· Give 1 point for each ✓.
Subtract 3 points for each X.

· The pair with more points wins.

Practice Ungrouping

Decide if you need to ungroup. If you need to ungroup,
draw a magnifying glass around the top number.
Then subtract.

1.
```
   5 4 9
 - 2 6 5
```

Ungroup to get 10 ones? _____

Ungroup to get 10 tens? _____

2.
```
   2 1 2
 - 1 1 8
```

Ungroup to get 10 ones? _____

Ungroup to get 10 tens? _____

3.
```
   9 2 1
 - 4 2 3
```

Ungroup to get 10 ones? _____

Ungroup to get 10 tens? _____

4.
```
   6 8 3
 - 3 7 7
```

Ungroup to get 10 ones? _____

Ungroup to get 10 tens? _____

5. The second grade class wants to
buy a poster for their classroom.
The poster costs $5.45. The class
has collected $1.87. How much
more do they need to collect?

6. A town is building a water park for
children. It will take 470 days to
finish the park. The builders have
been working for 284 days. How
many more days will they need to
work to complete the park?

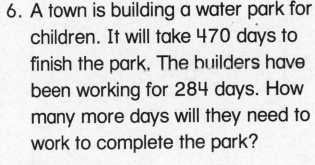

label

Match the equations with the correct Math Mountain.

1. $\boxed{} + 5 = 7$ •

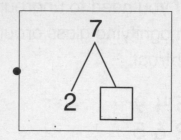

2. $2 + \boxed{} = 7$ •

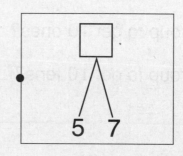

3. $5 + 7 = \boxed{}$ •

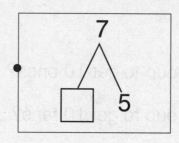

4. $\boxed{} - 5 = 2$ •

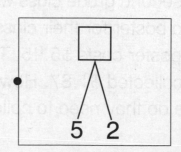

Match the word problems with the correct situation equation
and Math Mountains.

1.

| Hassan had some grapes. He ate 2 and had 6 left. How many did he have to start? |

$2 + \square = 6$

6
/ \
2   $\square$

2.

| Kim cut up 2 apples. Then she cut up 6 more. How many apples did she cut up in all? |

$2 + 6 = \square$

$\square$
/ \
2   6

3.

| Kayo put 2 fish in a bowl. Then he put in some more fish. Now there are 6 fish. How many more fish did Kayo put in the bowl? |

$\square - 2 = 6$

$\square$
/ \
2   6

4.

| Ali brings 6 carrots to the picnic. A rabbit eats some of her carrots. Now she has 2 carrots. How many carrots did the rabbit eat? |

$6 - \square = 2$

6
/ \
$\square$ 2

Name _____

Write word problems to match the proof drawings.

1.

```
        10 11 12 13
 9      ○○○○
        4
   ⌣_____⌣
   13 altogether
```

2.

```
        10 c
⊖⊖⊖⊖○ ○ ○○○○○
 3        7 left
```

3.

```
[○○○○]○ ○ ○○○○○
went home   still playing
```

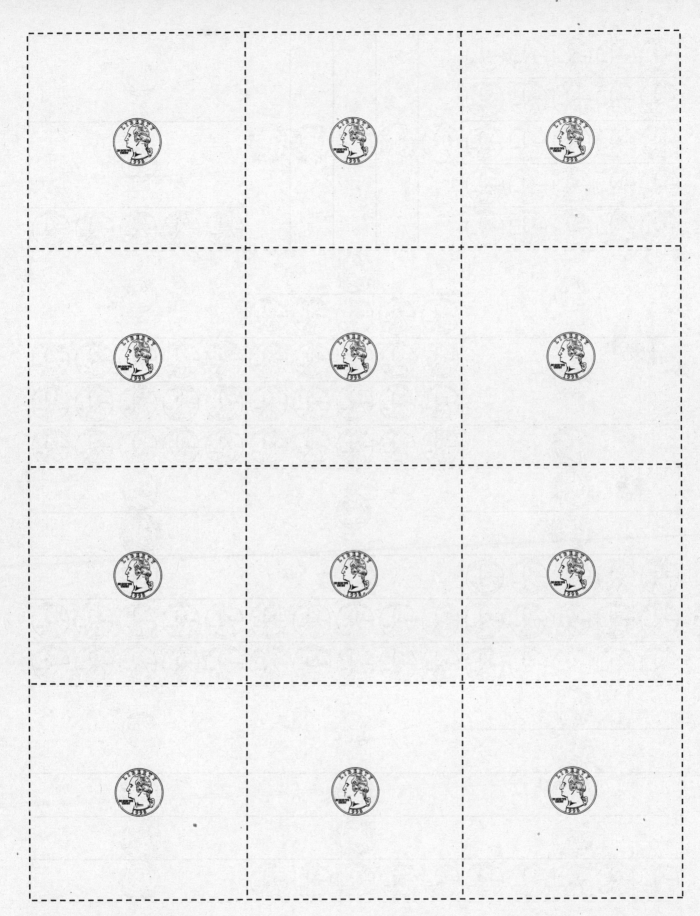

Cut on dashed lines.

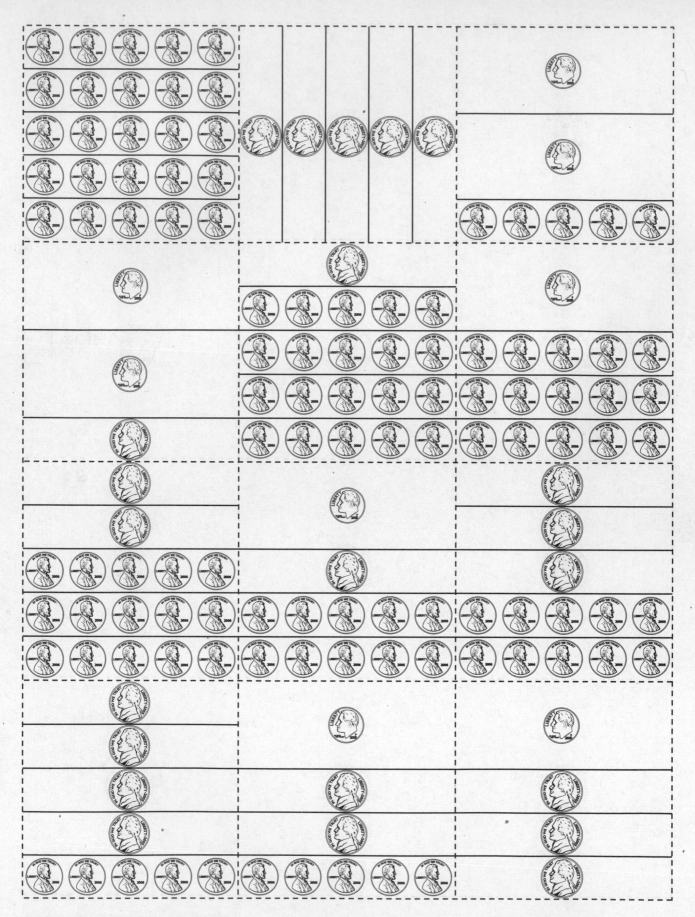

Cut on dashed lines **only.**

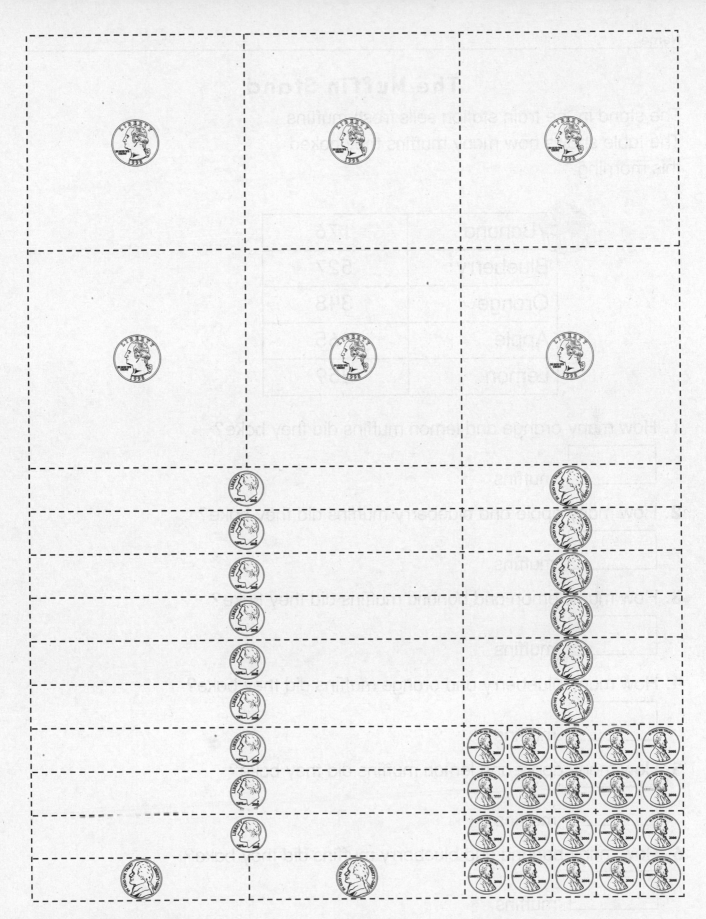

Cut on dashed lines.

The Muffin Stand

The stand in the train station sells fresh muffins.
The table shows how many muffins they baked
this morning.

Banana	176
Blueberry	527
Orange	348
Apple	465
Lemon	259

1. How many orange and lemon muffins did they bake?

☐ muffins

2. How many apple and blueberry muffins did they bake?

☐ muffins

3. How many lemon and banana muffins did they bake?

☐ muffins

4. How many blueberry and orange muffins did they bake?

☐ muffins

5. How many apple and lemon muffins did they bake?

☐ muffins

6. How many banana and blueberry muffins did they bake?

☐ muffins

Cut on dashed lines.

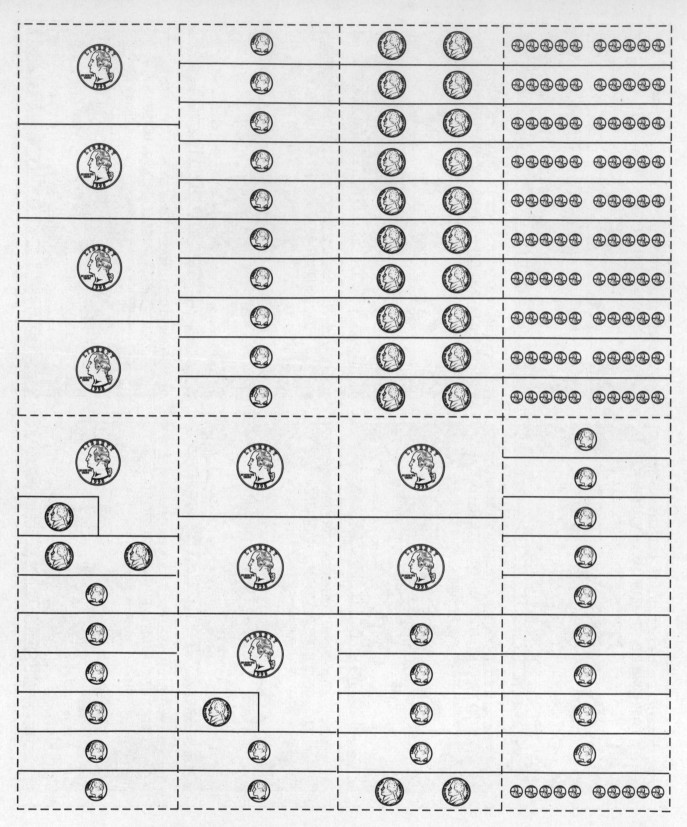

Cut on dashed lines **only.**

Draw comparison bars and ovals to match the information shown by the drawing.

1.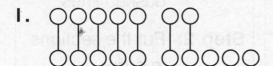

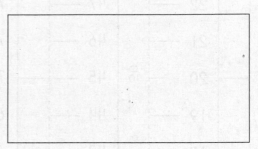

2.

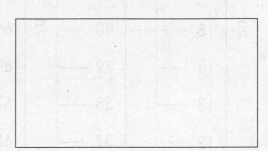

3.

4.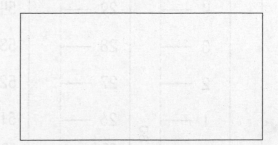

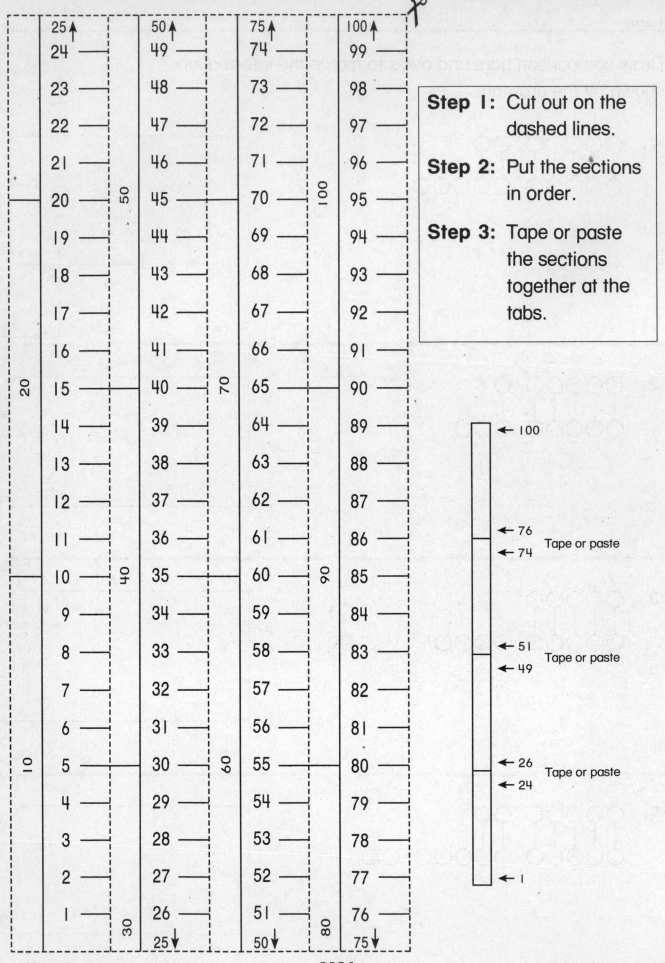

Step 1: Cut out on the dashed lines.

Step 2: Put the sections in order.

Step 3: Tape or paste the sections together at the tabs.

← 100

← 76
← 74   Tape or paste

← 51
← 49   Tape or paste

← 26
← 24   Tape or paste

← 1

Match the Math Mountains and comparison bars to the problems
on Homework and Remembering Page 31.

1.

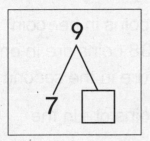

_____

2.

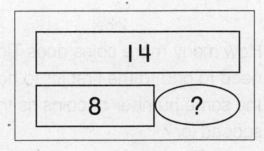

_____

3.

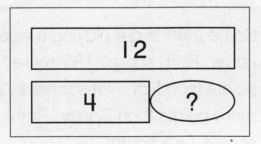

_____

4.

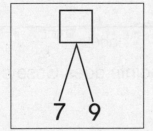

_____

Multistep Word Problems

Solve. Use a separate piece of paper to show your work.

1. There are 815 books for sale at the school book sale. 251 books were sold in the morning. Then 506 books were sold in the afternoon. How many books were not sold?

☐ _____
label

2. Tia has 922 coins in her coin collection. 438 coins are in one jar. The rest are in the second jar.

How many coins are in the second jar?

☐ _____
label

How many more coins does Tia need to add to the first jar to have the same number of coins as the second jar?

☐ _____
label

3. I have a book of 555 crossword puzzles. I solved 183 puzzles. My friend solved 279 puzzles. How many puzzles do we have left to solve?

☐ _____
label

4. Some friends are playing a video game. Ruth scores 189 more points than Nat. Nat scores 276 more points than Casey. Ruth scores 563 points.

How many points does Nat score?

☐ _____
label

How many points does Casey score?

☐ _____
label

Dive the Deep

$11 - 6 = \boxed{5}$ $12 - \boxed{6} = 6$ $13 - 8 = \boxed{5}$

$12 - 7 = \boxed{5}$ $17 - \boxed{8} = 9$ $15 - 6 = \boxed{9}$

$12 - 9 = \boxed{3}$ $13 - \boxed{5} = 8$ $11 - 9 = \boxed{2}$

$13 - 4 = \boxed{9}$ $14 - \boxed{6} = 8$ $13 - 9 = \boxed{4}$

$11 - 5 = \boxed{6}$ $17 - \boxed{9} = 8$ $15 - 7 = \boxed{8}$

$14 - 9 = \boxed{5}$ $11 - \boxed{8} = 3$ $14 - 8 = \boxed{6}$

$14 - 7 = \boxed{7}$ $12 - \boxed{4} = 8$ $12 - 5 = \boxed{7}$

$16 - 7 = \boxed{9}$ $16 - \boxed{8} = 8$ $11 - 3 = \boxed{8}$

$11 - 7 = \boxed{4}$ $15 - \boxed{7} = 8$ $13 - 6 = \boxed{7}$

$12 - 3 = \boxed{9}$ $16 - \boxed{9} = 7$ $18 - 9 = \boxed{9}$

$13 - 7 = \boxed{6}$ $11 - \boxed{4} = 7$ $12 - 8 = \boxed{4}$

Dive the Deep

$11 - 5 = \boxed{6}$ $12 - \boxed{6} = 6$ $13 - 5 = \boxed{8}$

$12 - 5 = \boxed{7}$ $17 - \boxed{9} = 8$ $15 - 9 = \boxed{6}$

$12 - 3 = \boxed{9}$ $13 - \boxed{8} = 5$ $11 - 2 = \boxed{9}$

$13 - 9 = \boxed{4}$ $14 - \boxed{8} = 6$ $13 - 4 = \boxed{9}$

$11 - 6 = \boxed{5}$ $17 - \boxed{8} = 9$ $15 - 8 = \boxed{7}$

$14 - 5 = \boxed{9}$ $11 - \boxed{3} = 8$ $14 - 6 = \boxed{8}$

$14 - 7 = \boxed{7}$ $12 - \boxed{8} = 4$ $12 - 7 = \boxed{5}$

$16 - 9 = \boxed{7}$ $16 - \boxed{8} = 8$ $11 - 8 = \boxed{3}$

$11 - 4 = \boxed{7}$ $15 - \boxed{8} = 7$ $13 - 7 = \boxed{6}$

$12 - 9 = \boxed{3}$ $16 - \boxed{7} = 9$ $18 - 9 = \boxed{9}$

$13 - 6 = \boxed{7}$ $11 - \boxed{7} = 4$ $12 - 4 = \boxed{8}$

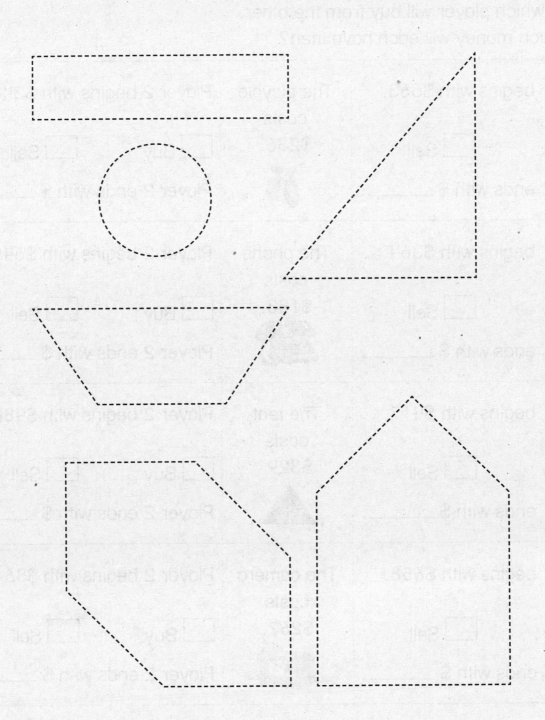

Buy or Sell?

Decide which player will buy from the other.
How much money will each have then?

Player 1 begins with $563. ☐ Buy ☐ Sell Player 1 ends with $ _____ .	The bicycle costs $236.	Player 2 begins with $348. ☐ Buy ☐ Sell Player 2 ends with $ _____ .
Player 1 begins with $364. ☐ Buy ☐ Sell Player 1 ends with $ _____ .	The phone costs $183.	Player 2 begins with $649. ☐ Buy ☐ Sell Player 2 ends with $ _____ .
Player 1 begins with $417. ☐ Buy ☐ Sell Player 1 ends with $ _____ .	The tent costs $329.	Player 2 begins with $488. ☐ Buy ☐ Sell Player 2 ends with $ _____ .
Player 1 begins with $658. ☐ Buy ☐ Sell Player 1 ends with $ _____ .	The camera costs $267.	Player 2 begins with $561. ☐ Buy ☐ Sell Player 2 ends with $ _____ .
Player 1 begins with $726. ☐ Buy ☐ Sell Player 1 ends with $ _____ .	The binoculars cost $255.	Player 2 begins with $439. ☐ Buy ☐ Sell Player 2 ends with $ _____ .

Buy or Sell?

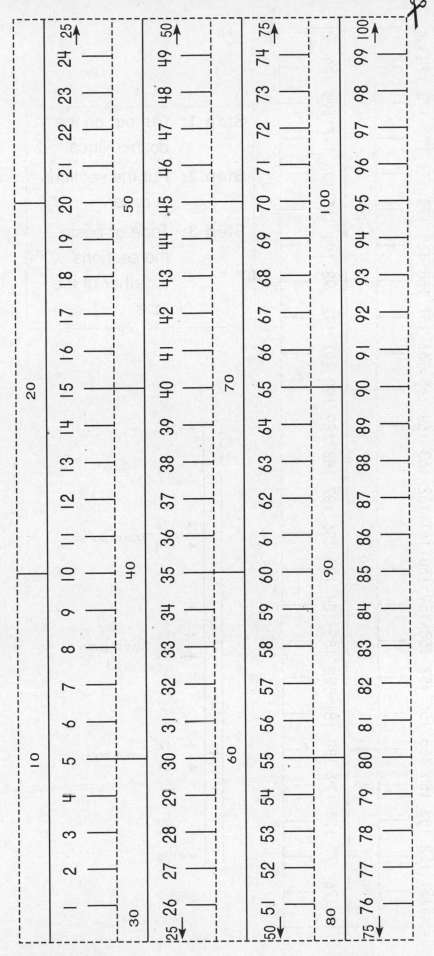

Step 1: Cut out on the dashed lines.

Step 2: Put the sections in order.

Step 3: Tape or paste the sections together at the tabs.

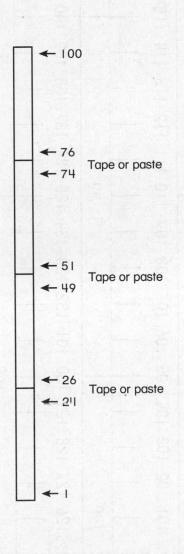

← 100

← 76
← 74   Tape or paste

← 51   Tape or paste
← 49

← 26   Tape or paste
← 24

← 1

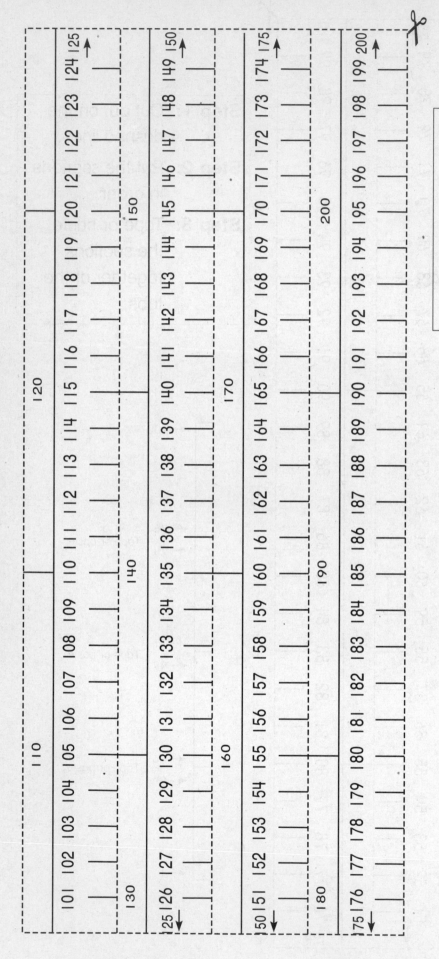

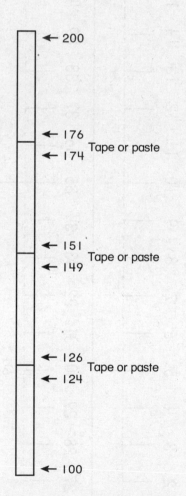

← 200

← 176 Tape or paste
← 174

← 151 Tape or paste
← 149

← 126 Tape or paste
← 124

← 100

Make a Yardstick

Directions:

Step 1: Cut along the dashed lines.

Step 2: Place the sections in the correct order.

Step 3: Tape or glue together the sections at the tab.

TAB	TAB	TAB	TAB	TAB	
	1 ft		2 ft		36 3 ft
5	11	17	23	29	35
4	10	16	22	28	34
3	9	15	21	27	33
2	8	14	20	26	32
1	7	13	19	25	31
0					

Make a Yardstick

Directions:

Step 1: Cut along the dashed lines.

Step 2: Place the sections in the correct order.

Step 3: Tape or glue together the sections at the tab.

TAB	TAB	TAB	TAB	TAB	
	4 ft		5 ft		72 6 ft
41	47	53	59	65	71
40	46	52	58	64	70
39	45	51	57	63	69
38	44	50	56	62	68
37	43	49	55	61	67
36					

Make a Yardstick

Directions:

Step 1: Cut along the dashed lines.

Step 2: Place the sections in the correct order.

Step 3: Tape or glue together the sections at the tab.

TAB	TAB	TAB	TAB	TAB	
	1 ft		2 ft		36 3 ft
5	11	17	23	29	35
4	10	16	22	28	34
3	9	15	21	27	33
2	8	14	20	26	32
1	7	13	19	25	31
0					

Make a Yardstick

Directions:

Step 1: Cut along the dashed lines.

Step 2: Place the sections in the correct order.

Step 3: Tape or glue together the sections at the tab.

TAB	TAB	TAB	TAB	TAB	
	4 ft		5 ft		72 6 ft
41	47	53	59	65	71
40	46	52	58	64	70
39	45	51	57	63	69
38	44	50	56	62	68
37	43	49	55	61	67
36					

0↗	0↗	0↗	0↗	0↗	0↗	0↗	0↗
1	1	1	1	1	1	1	1
2	2	2	2	2	2	2	2
3	3	3	3	3	3	3	3
4	4	4	4	4	4	4	4
5	5	5	5	5	5	5	5
6	6	6	6	6	6	6	6
7	7	7	7	7	7	7	7
8	8	8	8	8	8	8	8
9	9	9	9	9	9	9	9
10	**10**	**10**	**10**	**10**	**10**	**10**	**10**
11	11	11	11	11	11	11	11
12	12	12	12	12	12	12	12
13	13	13	13	13	13	13	13
14	14	14	14	14	14	14	14
15	15	15	15	15	15	15	15
16	16	16	16	16	16	16	16
17	17	17	17	17	17	17	17
18	18	18	18	18	18	18	18
19	19	19	19	19	19	19	19
20	**20**	**20**	**20**	**20**	**20**	**20**	**20**
21	21	21	21	21	21	21	21
22	22	22	22	22	22	22	22
23	23	23	23	23	23	23	23
24	24	24	24	24	24	24	24
25↘	25↘	25↘	25↘	25↘	25↘	25↘	25↘

Make an Inch Ruler

Directions:

Step 1: Cut along the dashed lines.

Step 2: Place the sections in the correct order.

Step 3: Tape or glue together the sections at the tab.

Step 4: Write a **6** where the two strips meet.

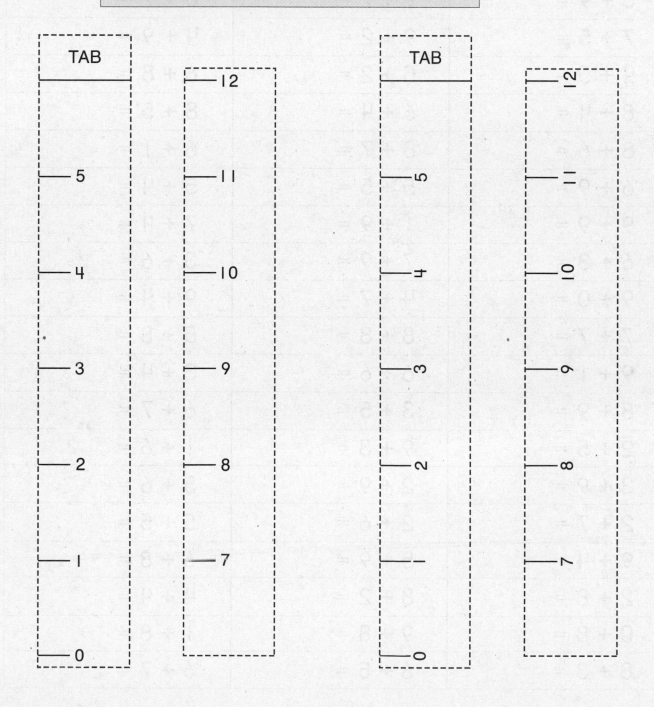

TAB

5

4

3

2

1

0

12

11

10

9

8

7

TAB

5

4

3

2

0

12

11

10

9

8

7

Addition Sprint

5 + 7 =	9 + 6 =	7 + 6 =
4 + 8 =	7 + 8 =	4 + 6 =
3 + 9 =	9 + 7 =	0 + 7 =
7 + 5 =	9 + 2 =	4 + 9 =
4 + 5 =	5 + 2 =	6 + 8 =
8 + 4 =	6 + 4 =	8 + 5 =
8 + 6 =	8 + 7 =	6 + 1 =
6 + 9 =	5 + 5 =	5 + 4 =
9 + 9 =	1 + 9 =	7 + 4 =
6 + 3 =	7 + 9 =	3 + 6 =
9 + 0 =	4 + 7 =	9 + 4 =
7 + 7 =	8 + 8 =	5 + 8 =
9 + 1 =	6 + 6 =	3 + 4 =
8 + 9 =	3 + 5 =	6 + 7 =
2 + 5 =	9 + 3 =	1 + 6 =
3 + 9 =	2 + 9 =	5 + 6 =
2 + 7 =	2 + 6 =	5 + 5 =
9 + 4 =	5 + 9 =	6 + 8 =
2 + 8 =	8 + 2 =	4 + 4 =
0 + 8 =	9 + 8 =	1 + 8 =
8 + 3 =	6 + 5 =	6 + 7 =

Ungroup Challenge

Work in 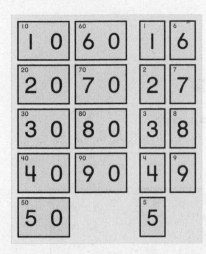. Lay out Secret Code Cards like this.

10 **1 0**	60 **6 0**	1 **1**	6 **6**
20 **2 0**	70 **7 0**	2 **2**	7 **7**
30 **3 0**	80 **8 0**	3 **3**	8 **8**
40 **4 0**	90 **9 0**	4 **4**	9 **9**
50 **5 0**		5 **5**	

1. Use Secret Code Cards to help you make a 2-digit subtraction (top number less than 100).

$$\begin{array}{r} \overset{5\ \ 12}{\cancel{62}} \\ -37 \\ \hline 25 \end{array}$$

60 **6 0**   2 **2**
30 **3 0**   7 **7**

2. Make another 2-digit subtraction.

- Use the same tens cards.

- If 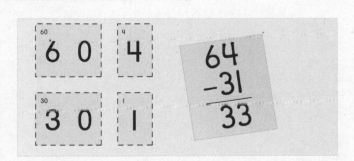 ungrouped a ten, use ones cards that *do not need more ones.*

$$\begin{array}{r} 64 \\ -31 \\ \hline 33 \end{array}$$

60 **6 0**   4 **4**
30 **3 0**   1 **1**

- If did not ungroup *a ten*, use ones cards that *need more ones.*

Activity continues on next page.

Ungroup Challenge (continued)

2. Work together to check your work. Correct any errors.

3. Put the Secret Code Cards back. Switch roles and repeat. Continue until time is up.

*To play as a game and compete with another pair, use the **Scoring Rules** below.*

Scoring Rules
for
Ungroup Challenge

- Trade papers with another pair.

- Put a ✓ next to each correct answer. Put an X next to each incorrect answer.

- Give I point for each ✓. Subtract 3 points for each X.

- The pair with more points wins.

Subtraction Sprint

7 – 4 =	10 – 6 =	17 – 9 =
13 – 5 =	15 – 9 =	6 – 4 =
9 – 3 =	11 – 3 =	10 – 7 =
11 – 2 =	18 – 9 =	13 – 9 =
8 – 6 =	8 – 4 =	12 – 5 =
12 – 9 =	9 – 7 =	16 – 8 =
6 – 3 =	13 – 6 =	14 – 7 =
15 – 7 =	12 – 3 =	10 – 6 =
10 – 8 =	16 – 7 =	8 – 5 =
8 – 3 =	7 – 5 =	11 – 9 =
14 – 5 =	12 – 4 =	13 – 7 =
11 – 7 =	17 – 8 =	14 – 8 =
10 – 4 =	9 – 4 =	10 – 5 =
12 – 8 =	14 – 8 =	12 – 6 =
16 – 9 =	11 – 4 =	15 – 7 =
14 – 6 =	9 – 6 =	13 – 6 =
9 – 5 =	12 – 7 =	11 – 8 =
13 – 9 =	14 – 9 =	12 – 3 =
10 – 3 =	13 – 4 =	13 – 5 =
15 – 8 =	7 – 3 =	15 – 6 =
11 – 5 =	11 – 6 =	13 – 8 =

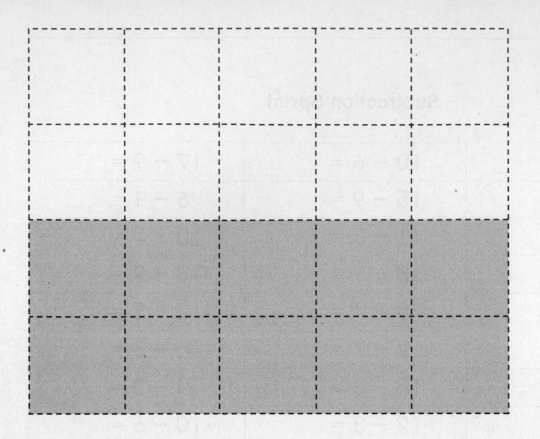

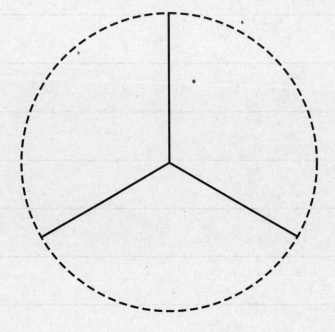

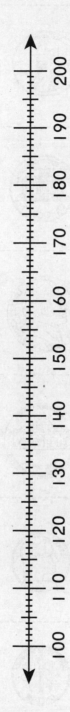

200
190
180
170
160
150
140
130
120
110
100

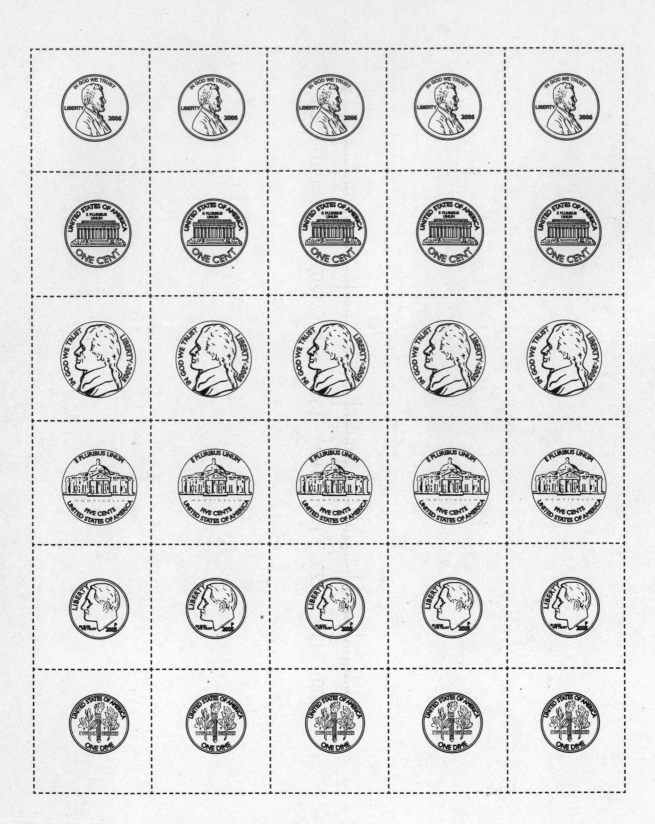

Identify Shapes

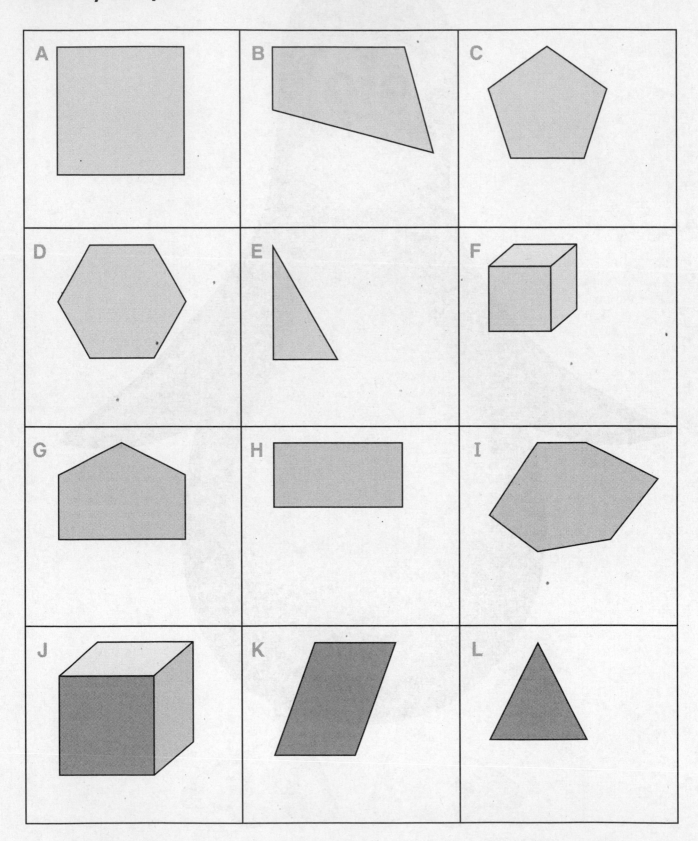

Name

Practice Ungrouping

Decide if you need to ungroup. If you need to ungroup, draw a magnifying glass around the top number. Then subtract.

1. 5 4 9
   −2 6 5
    2 8 4

Ungroup to get 10 ones? no
Ungroup to get 10 tens? yes

2. 2 1 2
   −1 1 8
      9 4

Ungroup to get 10 ones? yes
Ungroup to get 10 tens? yes

3. 9 2 1
   −4 2 3
    4 9 8

Ungroup to get 10 ones? yes
Ungroup to get 10 tens? yes

4. 6 8 3
   −3 7 7
    3 0 6

Ungroup to get 10 ones? yes
Ungroup to get 10 tens? no

5. The second grade class wants to buy a poster for their classroom. The poster costs $5.45. The class has collected $1.87. How much more do they need to collect?

$3.58

6. A town is building a water park for children. It will take 470 days to finish the park. The builders have been working for 284 days. How many more days will they need to work to complete the park?

186 more days
_____ label

Math Expressions
© Houghton Mifflin Harcourt Publishing Company

M53

Practice Ungrouping

Name

There are 15 hidden equations. None have a + sign or = sign.
Ring as many as you can find. Add the + and = signs.

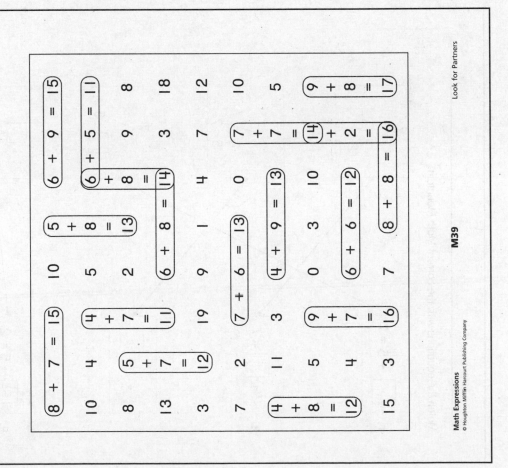

Math Expressions
© Houghton Mifflin Harcourt Publishing Company

M39

Look for Partners

Match the word problems with the correct situation equation and Math Mountains.

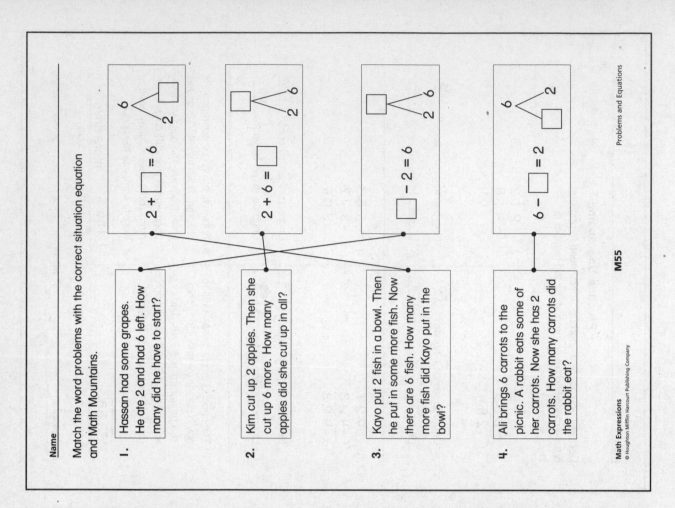

1. Hassan had some grapes. He ate 2 and had 6 left. How many did he have to start?

2. Kim cut up 2 apples. Then she cut up 6 more. How many apples did she cut up in all?

3. Kayo put 2 fish in a bowl. Then he put in some more fish. Now there are 6 fish. How many more fish did Kayo put in the bowl?

4. Ali brings 6 carrots to the picnic. A rabbit eats some of her carrots. Now she has 2 carrots. How many carrots did the rabbit eat?

M55   Problems and Equations

Match the equations with the correct Math Mountain.

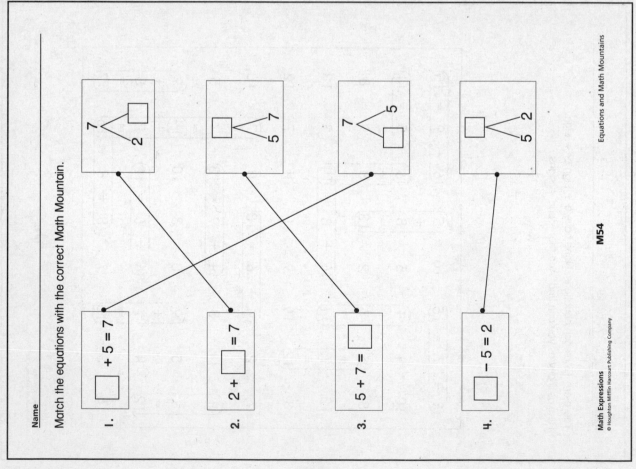

1. $\square + 5 = 7$

2. $2 + \square = 7$

3. $5 + 7 = \square$

4. $\square - 5 = 2$

M54   Equations and Math Mountains

Draw comparison bars and ovals to match the information shown by the drawing.

1.
| 10 | |
| 7 | 3 |

2.
| 8 | |
| 6 | 2 |

3.
| 9 | |
| 5 | 4 |

4.
| 12 | |
| 7 | 5 |

Comparison Drawings

The Muffin Stand

The stand in the train station sells fresh muffins. The table shows how many muffins they baked this morning.

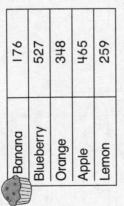

Banana	176
Blueberry	527
Orange	348
Apple	465
Lemon	259

1. How many orange and lemon muffins did they bake?
   607 muffins

2. How many apple and blueberry muffins did they bake?
   992 muffins

3. How many lemon and banana muffins did they bake?
   435 muffins

4. How many blueberry and orange muffins did they bake?
   875 muffins

5. How many apple and lemon muffins did they bake?
   724 muffins

6. How many banana and blueberry muffins did they bake?
   703 muffins

The Muffin Stand

Multistep Word Problems

Solve. Use a separate piece of paper to show your work.

1. There are 815 books for sale at the school book sale. 251 books were sold in the morning. Then 506 books were sold in the afternoon. How many books were not sold?

58 books
_____
label

2. Tia has 922 coins in her coin collection. 438 coins are in one jar. The rest are in the second jar.

How many coins are in the second jar?

484 coins
_____
label

How many more coins does Tia need to add to the first jar to have the same number of coins as the second jar?

46 more coins
_____
label

3. I have a book of 555 crossword puzzles. I solved 183 puzzles. My friend solved 279 puzzles. How many puzzles do we have left to solve?

93 puzzles
_____
label

4. Some friends are playing a video game. Ruth scores 189 more points than Nat. Nat scores 276 more points than Casey. Ruth scores 563 points.

How many points does Nat score?

374 points
_____
label

How many points does Casey score?

98 points
_____
label

Match the Math Mountains and comparison bars to the problems on Homework and Remembering Page 31.

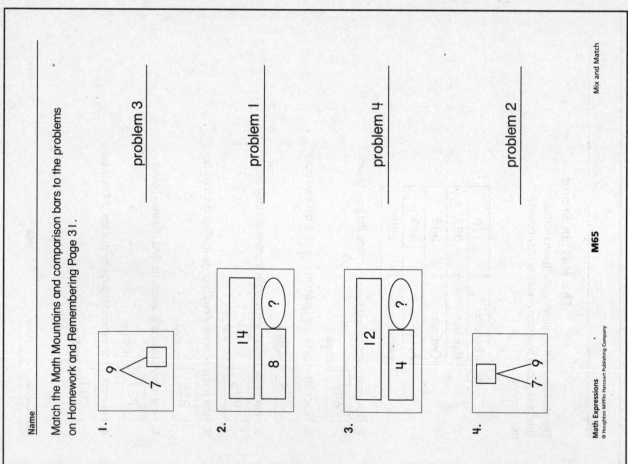

1. _____ problem 3

2. _____ problem 1

3. _____ problem 4

4. _____ problem 2

Subtraction Sprint

7 − 4 = 3	10 − 6 = 4	17 − 9 = 8
13 − 5 = 8	15 − 9 = 6	6 − 4 = 2
9 − 3 = 6	11 − 3 = 8	10 − 7 = 3
11 − 2 = 9	18 − 9 = 9	13 − 9 = 4
8 − 6 = 2	8 − 4 = 4	12 − 5 = 7
12 − 9 = 3	9 − 7 = 2	16 − 8 = 8
6 − 3 = 3	13 − 6 = 7	14 − 7 = 7
15 − 7 = 8	12 − 3 = 9	10 − 6 = 4
10 − 8 = 2	16 − 7 = 9	8 − 5 = 3
8 − 3 = 5	7 − 5 = 2	11 − 9 = 2
14 − 5 = 9	12 − 4 = 8	13 − 7 = 6
11 − 7 = 4	17 − 8 = 9	14 − 8 = 6
10 − 4 = 6	9 − 4 = 5	10 − 5 = 5
12 − 8 = 4	14 − 8 = 6	12 − 6 = 6
16 − 9 = 7	11 − 4 = 7	15 − 7 = 8
14 − 6 = 8	9 − 6 = 3	13 − 6 = 7
9 − 5 = 4	12 − 7 = 5	11 − 8 = 3
13 − 9 = 4	14 − 9 = 5	12 − 3 = 9
10 − 3 = 7	13 − 4 = 9	13 − 5 = 8
15 − 8 = 7	7 − 3 = 4	15 − 6 = 9
11 − 5 = 6	11 − 6 = 5	13 − 8 = 5

Addition Sprint

5 + 7 = 12	9 + 6 = 15	7 + 6 = 13
4 + 8 = 12	7 + 8 = 15	4 + 6 = 10
3 + 9 = 12	9 + 7 = 16	0 + 7 = 7
7 + 5 = 12	9 + 2 = 11	4 + 9 = 13
4 + 5 = 9	5 + 2 = 7	6 + 8 = 14
8 + 4 = 12	6 + 4 = 10	8 + 5 = 13
8 + 6 = 14	8 + 7 = 15	6 + 1 = 7
6 + 9 = 15	5 + 5 = 10	5 + 4 = 9
9 + 9 = 18	1 + 9 = 10	7 + 4 = 11
6 + 3 = 9	7 + 9 = 16	3 + 6 = 9
9 + 0 = 9	4 + 7 = 11	9 + 4 = 13
7 + 7 = 14	8 + 8 = 16	5 + 8 = 13
9 + 1 = 10	6 + 6 = 12	3 + 4 = 7
8 + 9 = 17	3 + 5 = 8	6 + 7 = 13
2 + 5 = 7	9 + 3 = 12	1 + 6 = 7
3 + 9 = 12	2 + 9 = 11	5 + 6 = 11
2 + 7 = 9	2 + 6 = 8	5 + 5 = 10
9 + 4 = 13	5 + 9 = 14	6 + 8 = 14
2 + 8 = 10	8 + 2 = 10	4 + 4 = 8
0 + 8 = 8	9 + 8 = 17	1 + 8 = 9
8 + 3 = 11	6 + 5 = 11	6 + 7 = 13